UNDERSTANDING COMPUTER-AIDED DESIGN AND DRAFTING

David L. Goetsch

UNDERSTANDING COMPUTER-AIDED DESIGN AND DRAFTING

David L. Goetsch

PennWell Books

COMPUTER GRAPHICS WORLD

PennWell Publishing Company
Tulsa, Oklahoma USA

DEDICATION

This book is dedicated to Dr. J.E. McCracken for nine years of patient teaching and encouragement.

Copyright © 1986 by
PennWell Publishing Company
1421 South Sheridan Road/P.O. Box 1260
Tulsa, Oklahoma 74101

Library of Congress Cataloging-in-Publication Data

Goetsch, David L.
  Understanding computer-aided design and drafting.

  Includes index.
  1. Computer graphics. 2. Computer-aided design.
I. Title.
T385.G635   1986   620'.00425'0285   85-28393
ISBN 0-87814-300-9

Printed in the United States of America

1   2   3   4   5   90   89   88   87   86

CONTENTS

PREFACE

Understanding Computer-Aided Design and Drafting was written in response to a need for a simply written, basic book for practitioners. There are numerous books about CADD on the market, but they deal with the needs of CADD students in high schools, technical schools, colleges, and universities. I know; I've written several of them myself.

However, the needs of inexperienced CADD students and experienced, employed practitioners are not exactly the same. This book was written to speak to those special needs of the practitioner.

WHO IS THIS BOOK FOR?

Understanding Computer-Aided Design and Drafting has value for various groups of people, all of whom have individual reasons for needing more knowledge about CADD and all of whom have individual needs in terms of specific knowledge about CADD. Some groups that will find this book particularly helpful are:

Drafters
Checkers
Designers
Drafting supervisors
Drafting managers
Architects
Engineers
Engineering managers
Manufacturing personnel
Computer sales personnel
Marketing representatives for CADD vendors
Management-level personnel for CADD vendors
Drafting teachers at all levels
Engineering professors
Architecture professors
Students of CADD management
Students of engineering management
Vendor training personnel

PURPOSE AND GOALS OF THE BOOK

The purpose of this book is to help make those people listed in the previous section, as well as anyone else who might read it, "CADD-literate." What is a CADD-literate person? That's easy; it is a person who knows everything in this book!

In attempting to help people become CADD-literate, *Understanding Computer-Aided Design and Drafting* provides readers with everything a CADD-literate person needs to know about the following topics:

1. The computer
2. Evolution of design and drafting to its current state of involvement with computers
3. Structure of the CADD system
4. Operation of a CADD system
5. CADD vendors and their systems
6. Justifying a CADD conversion
7. Implementing a CADD conversion
8. Planning, presenting, and evaluating CADD training
9. Advanced CADD concepts
10. Future development

SPECIAL FEATURES OF THE BOOK

Understanding Computer-Aided Design and Drafting has several special features that make it a particularly valuable aid to learning. The most important of these features are as follows:

- The book is written in simple, conversational language, making it easy to understand.
- The book contains numerous everyday examples that make complex concepts much easier to understand.
- The book is well illustrated with a broad range of drawings and photographs.
- The chapters are logically sequenced so that learning in one is built upon learning from the previous one.
- The book contains helpful checklists and sample instruments that can be used in justifying and implementing CADD as well as in planning, presenting, participating in, and evaluating CADD training.

- The book contains a comprehensive glossary of CADD terms for reference.
- The book contains a comprehensive index for easy access to specific material.

COMPARISON WITH OTHER CADD BOOKS

Typically the first books on CADD to reach the market have been designed as textbooks for students studying to become technicians, architects, or engineers. The books must necessarily approach the subject from a student's perspective and speak to the specific needs of students.

What is missing from these other books is in-depth material on such topics as how to justify a CADD conversion in financial terms; how to actually implement a CADD conversion and make it work; how to develop, present, and evaluate training for buyers if the reader is a vendor; and how to develop and present training for students and practitioners if the reader is an educator in a school, college, or university.

Understanding Computer-Aided Design and Drafting covers all these things and much more. And it does so in simple, down-to-earth language.

CHAPTER-BY-CHAPTER ANALYSIS

Chapter 1 is an overview of computers. This is important because in order to understand computer-aided design and drafting, one must first understand computers. This chapter helps readers develop enough of an understanding of computers to be able to learn about CADD.

Chapter 2 traces the development of drafting and design from T-squares to CADD. This chapter helps readers gain a perspective on CADD and where it fits into the overall development of design and drafting as a profession. It also relates CADD to the design process and compares manual design and drafting with CADD.

Chapter 3 helps readers understand the various components of a CADD system. Readers will learn about hardware, software, and users, and how these three components interact to become a CADD system.

Chapter 4 teaches readers in generic terms the fundamentals of how design and drafting tasks are performed on a CADD system. This chapter is helpful in answering that question that all drafters and designers have the first time they confront a CADD system: "How do I make it do what I want it to do?"

Chapter 5 profiles over twenty of the top CADD vendors and their systems. This is important, not for the specifics that go with a given system, but because a CADD-literate person should know the names of the leading CADD vendors, the systems they market, and the approximate cost of the systems.

Chapter 6 shows readers how to justify the CADD conversion in financial terms. This is important because management is not likely to authorize an investment in CADD just because CADD systems make better-looking drawings. Management will want bottom-line answers to some tough nuts-and-bolts questions. This chapter helps readers learn how to come up with those answers.

Chapter 7 shows readers how to implement a CADD conversion and make it work. The success or failure of CADD will be determined to a great extent by the manner in which the conversion is handled; if handled improperly, a CADD conversion can turn out to be a very expensive flop. This chapter helps readers learn how to avoid such a problem and have a successful conversion.

Chapter 8 covers planning, presenting, and evaluating CADD training. It is designed especially for vendor personnel and educators responsible for CADD training for their companies and schools. This is a lengthy chapter, as it should be. Training may be the most important aspect of a CADD conversion, yet it typically receives less attention than it deserves. Vendors need to know how to present high-quality training that will ensure buyers not only accept CADD but become highly skilled, innovative CADD system users. Educational institutions need to be offering CADD training both on a job preparatory basis and on an updating basis for employed practitioners. This chapter will help both groups. And it will help the recipients of CADD training see what they should expect from a vendor or a school.

Chapter 9 covers several advanced CADD concepts that a CADD-literate person should be familiar with.

Chapter 10 explains where CADD is going between now and the year 2000. It goes into depth on the trend toward microCADD.

Understanding Computer-Aided Design and Drafting was purposely designed to have a broad appeal and varied usefulness. Many people want and need to know more about CADD, whether it be to undergo a CADD conversion on the job, market CADD products, or teach CADD courses. I hope that this book will speak to the needs of these individuals in a language that is easy to understand. Good luck with your learning!

David L. Goetsch

Chapter 1
OVERVIEW OF COMPUTERS

The first step in learning about computer-aided design and drafting (CADD) is to learn about computers. You don't need to be a computer expert or even a "hacker." You just need to be literate with regard to computers. Once you are literate about computers, learning CADD will be easy.

This chapter presumes absolutely no prior computer knowledge on the part of readers, but you should study it closely even if you have a little computer knowledge. Don't skip ahead! Trying to learn about CADD without first learning about computers is like trying to build a house without first laying the foundation.

This chapter represents the foundation upon which your understanding of CADD will be built during successive chapters in the book. It answers several important questions:

1. What is a computer?
2. What is hardware?
3. What is software?
4. What are users?
5. How do humans communicate with computers?
6. What are micros, minis, mainframes, and supers?
7. Who started the computer revolution?
8. Is there anybody left who doesn't use a computer?
9. If computers are so good, what's all the fuss about?

WHAT IS A COMPUTER?

A computer is a machine. A machine is a structure or device consisting of various parts designed to work together to perform some type of task. A lathe is a machine. A mill is a machine. A drill press is a machine. I know what you're thinking. If a computer is just another machine, what's all the fuss about? I once used this example in a workshop and a drafting manager stopped me to say, "All I hear these days is computer revolution this and computer revolution that. Now you say a computer is just a machine. A drill press is a machine, but I don't hear everyone talking about the drill press revolution!"

He had a good point. Like a drill press or a lathe or a mill, the computer is a machine. Each of these machines consists of various parts designed to work together to perform some type of task. Then what separates the computer from other machines? The answer: The computer has four characteristics that set it apart from other machines:

1. The computer performs all tasks electronically.
2. The computer has internal storage capabilities.
3. The computer receives operational instructions from stored programs.
4. The computer can modify program executions by making logical decisions.

Now that you understand what separates the computer from other less-glamorous machines, you are ready for a concise definition of "computer." A **computer is an electronic machine with storage, logic, and mathematical capabilities that can perform work extremely fast.** The functional words in this definition are "extremely fast." The computer can do in milliseconds what would take humans hours, days, and in some cases weeks. Now that you know what a computer is, let's learn how humans and computers compare.

Humans and Computers

Do you play tennis or even just watch an occasional tennis match? If so, you know that a good doubles team results when the partners have offsetting strengths and weaknesses. This same concept of offsetting strength and weakness makes the human-computer team very effective.

Computers do well those things that humans do poorly. Humans, on the other hand, do well those things that computers do poorly. Every job consists of performing various work tasks that make up the job. Several factors are important in performing work tasks no matter what the job is. These factors include speed, reliability, accuracy, reason, judgment, intuition, and common sense (Figure 1–1). What supervisor wouldn't give almost anything for all employees to be endowed with generous amounts of these attributes?

Consider how important these factors are on the job. **Speed** is important. When was the last time you worked on a project that didn't need to be com-

FACTORS	COMPUTERS	HUMANS
SPEED	STRENGTH	WEAKNESS
RELIABILITY	STRENGTH	WEAKNESS
ACCURACY	STRENGTH	WEAKNESS
REASON	WEAKNESS	STRENGTH
JUDGMENT	WEAKNESS	STRENGTH
INTUITION	WEAKNESS	STRENGTH
COMMON SENSE	WEAKNESS	STRENGTH

Figure 1–1 Important factors in getting work done

pleted yesterday? The work world is in a perpetual state of hurry-up. For this reason, success has always come to those who can devise ways to get more work done properly in less time. This is the "productivity" issue, and it is the reason that, since the dawn of civilization, better and better machines have been invented generation after generation. Computers are the latest in a long list of machines invented to improve productivity, and they are effective in doing so—more effective, in fact, than any machines that preceded them. Computers can do in milliseconds what would take humans weeks. Speed is one of the strengths the computer brings to the human-computer team.

Reliability is important in getting work done. Unfortunately, it is a serious human weakness. A human will have a bad night and come to work late. Humans take coffee breaks. Humans stretch a lunch hour to an hour-and-a-half. Humans leave work early. Humans have good days and bad days in unpredictable patterns. In short, humans are not very reliable. Computers, on the other hand, don't have bad days or bad nights, don't take coffee breaks, don't stretch lunch hours, and don't leave work early. In other words, computers are very reliable. So reliability is a strength computers bring to the human-computer team.

Accuracy is important in getting work done. Unfortunately, again, humans are not very accurate. Human accuracy tends to decrease as fatigue and boredom increase. Computers, on the other hand, don't get tired or bored. And they are very accurate. Accuracy is yet another strength computers bring to the human-computer team.

So far so good for the computer. It is fast, reliable, and accurate. Humans can be slow, unreliable, and inaccurate. In fact, if these three factors were all that mattered in getting work done, we could say, "Move aside, humans, and let the computers take over!" But luckily for us, these factors are not all that matters. In fact, of the various factors that are important, these don't even rank at the top of the list. Now let's see what humans bring to the team.

Reason and **Judgment** are important. Computers don't have either of these vital characteristics. There are standard operating procedures (SOPs) for nearly every job, but how many times a day do we confront situations not covered by SOPs? For computers, confronting a situation not covered in the SOP (its programs) is an impossible situation. Computers simply cannot handle such occurrences. But for humans, this is an everyday situation to which they easily respond because they have reasoning and judgment capabilities.

To illustrate just how inadequate computers are in situations requiring reason or judgment, I'll use an everyday example. Mr. Jones is a drafting manager for a large manufacturing firm. He has two secretaries who work on alternate days—Ms. Human and Mr. Computer. It's Monday morning, and Mr. Jones had a bad weekend. He buzzes the secretary on his intercom. "I have a terrible headache this morning. Bring me a thousand aspirin tablets, please, and hurry!"

If Ms. Human is on duty when Mr. Jones buzzes, she will know that he is exaggerating and will bring him two aspirin tablets, not a thousand. She will also bring a cup of coffee or water and place it and the aspirins on the boss's desk—very quietly. However, if Mr. Computer responds to the intercom message, the boss will get 1,000 aspirin tablets, no water, no coffee, no quiet, and no sympathy. Computers cannot reason or make judgments. They can only do as they are told—precisely and literally. So reason and judgment are strengths that humans bring to the human-computer team.

Intuition and **Common Sense** are important in getting work done. Humans have these attributes (at least most do); computers don't. How many times have you made decisions based on "gut feelings"? This is intuition. Some of the best decisions are based on intuition and common sense. Humans have it; computers don't. Another everyday example illustrates this.

Suppose a football coach sizes up the situation and tells his quarterback to throw a pass on the next play. The quarterback calls a pass play in the huddle and breaks. The ball is snapped, and everyone runs the proper patterns. However, as the play evolves, it becomes evident that the defense was looking for just such a play and all receivers are covered. If the quarterback is human, he or she knows instinctively either to run the ball or to throw it out of bounds. This is just common sense. However, if the quarterback is a computer, the pass play will be run, even though the receivers are covered, and an interception will probably result. Computers don't have intuition or common sense. If computers did play football as in the example above, a scouting report on one might read, "Good speed, accurate, and reliable, but dumb!" Thus, common sense and intuition are strengths that humans bring to the human-computer team.

To summarize the comparison, computers are fast, reliable, and accurate; humans aren't. Humans have reason, judgment capabilities, intuition, and common sense; computers don't. By themselves, humans and computers are not very good at getting work done. But working as a team they are unbeatable!

Now that you know the strengths and weaknesses of humans and computers, you are ready to learn about the different categories of computers. Notice I have said "categories," not sizes. Sizes are dealt with later.

Categories of Computers

Computers are either digital or analog. You will probably never have occasion to even see an analog computer. The computers that humans use in most situations are digital computers. However, a computer-literate person must, at least, know that there are two categories of computers and what they are called.

A **digital computer** receives input in the form of numbers, letters, and special characters. In other words, a digital computer receives input from a keyboard similar to the keyboard of a typewriter. Input is the generic name given to anything entered into the computer. Input into a digital computer is received and stored as electrical impulses or signals called binary digits—hence the name "digital computer."

An **analog computer** doesn't deal with numbers, letters, and characters, and it doesn't accept input from a keyboard. Rather, analog computers are used to measure continuous physical magnitudes such as heat, light, pressure, fluid flow, and current. Such a computer might be used in regulating the fuel flow in a modern automobile or the climate control system of a large office building.

The most important thing to remember about analog computers is that they are not the type that you are concerned with. You will use digital computers in CADD and will learn only about digital computers in this book.

Let me share a little trick you can use to impress your friends with your computer knowledge. One way to illustrate the difference between digital and analog computers is to use the example of clocks. Older clocks always had analog faces (numbers and hands). More modern clocks are apt to have digital readouts, shown in Figure 1–2. The next time you see a friend with and old-fashioned watch, tell him, "I see you still wear an analog watch." If he looks confused, you can impress him with your computer knowledge by telling him about digital and analog faces. However, if he doesn't look confused and starts saying things like "RAM," "ROM," and "megabytes," you'd better break off the conversation until you've read the rest of this chapter.

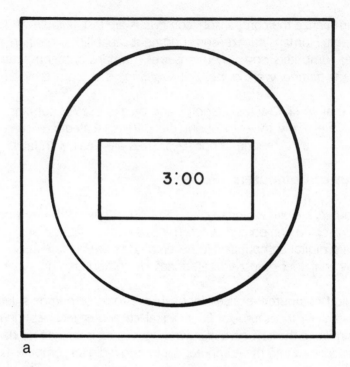

a

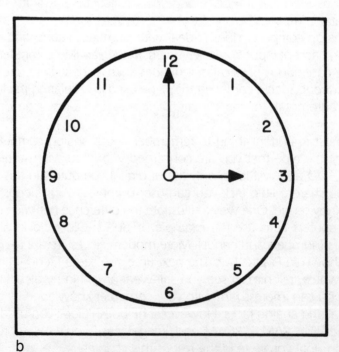

b

Figure 1–2   Digitial **(a)** versus analog **(b)** concept

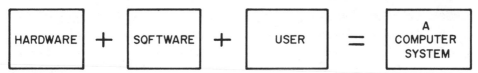

Figure 1–3   Components of a complete computer system

What has been covered so far is all you need to know about what a computer is. You are now ready to learn about two of the most frequently used words in the English language: hardware and software. We talk a lot about the computer these days, but what we actually use on the job is a computer system. The computer by itself can't do much for us. A computer system consists of three major components: hardware, software, and the user, as indicated in Figure 1–3.

WHAT IS HARDWARE?

When you look at a computer system, you are looking at **hardware.** The machines in the system are the hardware. Computer system hardware can be divided into subcomponents in any one of several ways. Probably the easiest to

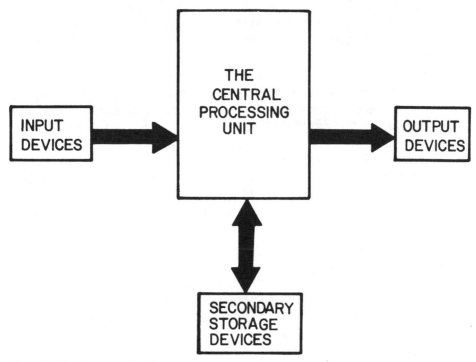

Figure 1–4   Computer hardware

understand is the four-component approach: input devices, output devices, secondary storage devices, and the central processing unit (CPU), shown in Figure 1–4.

The most important of these components is the CPU. It is the brain of the system. In fact, it is the computer in a computer system. All other hardware components are **peripheral devices.** As the name implies, a "peripheral" is any other device in a computer system other than the CPU. Peripherals allow humans to interact with computers.

The Central Processing Unit (CPU)

The central processing unit in a computer system is usually referred to as the CPU in everyday conversation. The CPU consists of three components: the arithmetic/logic section, the control section, and interfacing mechanisms. Another component, the internal storage unit, is often housed in the same cabinet as the CPU, seen in Figure 1–5.

The arithmetic/logic section of the CPU performs all arithmetic functions such as addition, subtraction, multiplication, and division. It also compares data, moves data, and sets up the conditions for logical decisions. Addition, subtraction, multiplication, and division speak for themselves. Examples of comparisons of data that might take place in the arithmetic/logic section are "greater than," "less than," "equal to," "less than or equal to," and "greater than or equal to." A logic decision that might occur in the arithmetic/logic section is IF A equals B, THEN add; IF A is less than B, THEN subtract.

The control section of the CPU stores programs and directs all operations of the system. The arithmetic/logic section will add and subtract numbers, but only as directed by the control section. As its name implies, the control section directs all input and output operations, transfers data to and from storage, and directs all arithmetic/logic operations.

Interfacing mechanisms are those devices that allow the CPU to **interface** with input, output, and secondary storage devices or, in other words, with peripherals. "Interface" used as a verb means to join two separate elements. Used as a noun, it means the medium by which this is done. Of course "output" is the opposite of input. It means anything that comes out of the computer for human use.

The internal storage unit is called a number of different things in everyday conversation. Most frequently it is referred to as the "main memory," "memory," "primary storage," "main storage," or just "storage." The internal storage unit serves the same purpose as a closet, garage, or filing cabinet. It is a place to store things until they are needed.

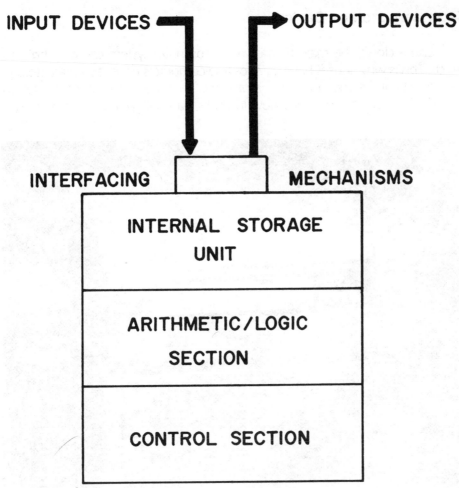

Figure 1–5 A central processing unit (CPU) with internal storage unit

The things that are stored in the internal storage unit are data. We've already used this word several times but haven't talked about what it means, and it is an important word in the vocabulary of a computer-literate person. Data are representations of facts, figures, or concepts in either human- or computer-useable form. In human-useable form, data are represented by numbers, letters, and special characters. In computer-useable form, data are represented by electrical impulses or binary digits. You will hear the term "alphanumeric data" used a lot around computers. These are data that consist of numbers, letters, and special characters, as opposed to "graphic data," which are pictorial representations of data. The chapters on CADD will deal with graphic data and alphanumeric data.

Secondary Storage Devices

Like a closet, the main memory of a computer system can only hold so much. This is why houses have garages and computers have secondary storage devices. What do you do when your closet is stuffed with all of the tennis rackets, golf clubs, fishing poles, bowling balls, baseball gloves, and old running

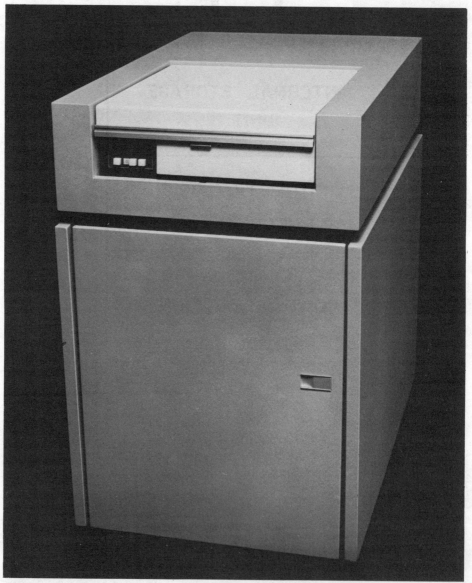

Figure 1–6   Disk drive unit for a minicomputer *(Courtesy ComputerVision)*

Figure 1–7 Disk drives built for a microcomputer *(Courtesy Radio Shack)*

shoes it will hold, and you need a place to store that box of worn-out record albums you never play but can't stand to part with? That's right! You put it in the garage. In this case, the garage is being used for secondary storage.

Computer systems also require secondary storage as an alternative when the main memory is full or to keep it from getting full. Secondary storage is sometimes referred to as auxiliary storage. Secondary storage devices in the current state of technology are either disk drives or tape drives (Figures 1–6 and 1–7). Data are stored magnetically on either disks or tapes. Small disks are referred to as diskettes.

Input/Output Devices

The hardware components discussed so far either store or process data. Before data can be stored or processed, though, they must be entered into the system or input.

Before data that have been stored and processed can be used, they must be taken out of the computer in human-useable form. This is known as the output process.

Input and output (I/O) operations are performed using many different input/output devices. The most familiar are the keyboard (input), printer (output), and magnetic tape unit (input/output). If a device is used strictly for input, it is classified as an input device; one used strictly for output is classified as an output device. A device that can be used for both is called an input/output device.

This is all you need to know for now about hardware. It's now time for you to learn about software and users.

WHAT IS SOFTWARE?

Software is the generic term used to describe the nonmechanical components of a computer system with the exception of users, which of course are human. These components include the programs, documentation, and reference manuals that go with the system.

Programs are specially coded instructions that direct the computer in performing all operations. People who are specially trained to write programs are called "computer programmers." **Documentation** consists of flow charts, block diagrams, and miscellaneous notes about the programs. **Reference manuals** include both technical manuals and user manuals.

Although software in the strictest sense of the word includes programs, documentation, and manuals, when most people use the word in everyday conversation, they are talking about programs only.

There are two basic types of software: system software and applications software. A good way to understand the difference between the two is to think of system software as being general-purpose software and applications software as being for specific purposes. Figure 1–8 depicts a comparison of the two types of software.

The general purposes performed by system software are those that are intrinsic to all computer operations. These include allowing data to be input, allowing the computer to store data, allowing the computer to process data, and allowing the computer to output data. The specific purposes performed by applications software are limitless and range from inventory control for large manufacturing firms to home computer games played in the den.

The line between computer hardware and software would seem to be a clear, distinct, black-and-white line. However, this is not really the case. The more advanced that computer technology becomes, the less distinct the line between hardware and software. The "gray area" separating hardware and software is often referred to as **firmware.**

Firmware is the name given to special stored programs designed to make a computer more flexible. Certain general operations that are repeated con-

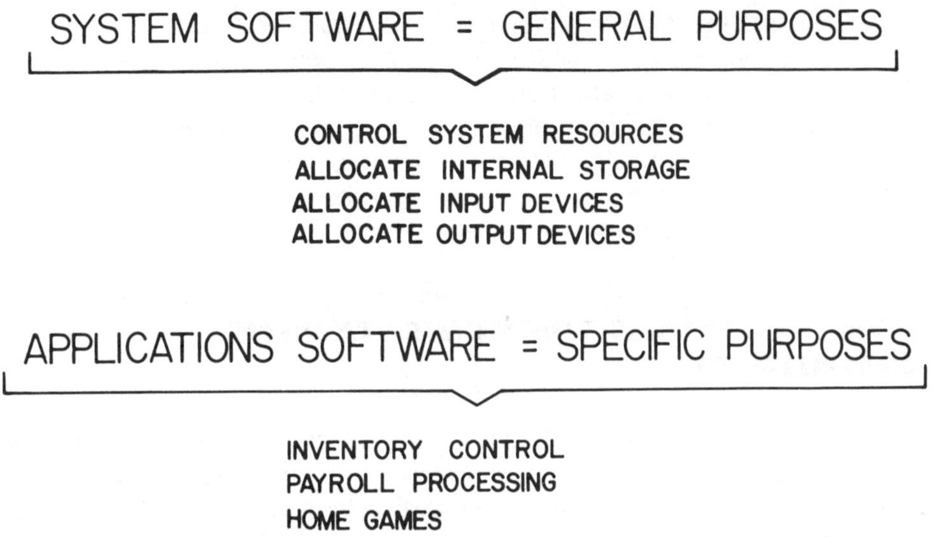

SYSTEM SOFTWARE = GENERAL PURPOSES

CONTROL SYSTEM RESOURCES
ALLOCATE INTERNAL STORAGE
ALLOCATE INPUT DEVICES
ALLOCATE OUTPUT DEVICES

APPLICATIONS SOFTWARE = SPECIFIC PURPOSES

INVENTORY CONTROL
PAYROLL PROCESSING
HOME GAMES

Figure 1–8   System and application software

stantly, such as math operations, can be wired into a computer's circuitry. However, the more functions that are wired in, the less flexible the computer becomes. On the other hand, if all functions were placed on programs and stored in the computer's main memory, the memory wouldn't be able to store any data except the programs.

This problem is solved by firmware. Firmware consists of microprograms or microcode stored in a special place called ROM (Read Only Memory). ROM is only used to store the microprograms that make up the firmware for a computer system. On this firmware are the instructions for operations that otherwise would be wired into the computer. Since firmware consists of programs instead of wired-in circuits, it can be tailor-made to fit the needs of individual applications. This makes the computer very flexible and allows computer manufacturers to market their products to a wide variety of clients.

ROM does not change the size of the main memory of the computer, and microprograms stored in ROM cannot be altered as those in the main memory can. This is what "Read Only Memory" means. Instructions may only be read; they cannot be written to, or changed.

WHAT IS A USER?

A user is anyone who uses a computer for any reason. Are computer programmers users? Yes. Do users have to be programmers? No! In fact, the overwhelming majority are not. If computer users had to be computer programmers, the computer revolution wouldn't have amounted to even a skirmish.

Children who play computer games are users. Students who receive instruction via computers are users. Secretaries who do word processing are users. Anyone who uses a computer for work or play is a user.

To users, a computer is a machine that makes them more productive or opens new horizons in the area of leisure. It's not magic and it's not mysterious—once you get used to it.

HOW DO HUMANS COMMUNICATE WITH COMPUTERS?

Talking to a computer is like talking to a person from a foreign country: you've got to speak his language. Computers are very much like people when it comes to communication; most speak only one language, although a few are multilingual.

Humans communicate with computers through written programs that are written in the language or languages that the computers understand. You don't need to be able to write programs in any of the various computer languages, but you should be able to name several different languages and explain how they are used.

Some of the most frequently used computer programming languages are BASIC, COBOL, FORTRAN, RPG, PASCAL, APL, and PL/1. In addition to programming languages, there are also machine and assembler languages.

BASIC stands for Beginner's All-purpose Symbolic Instructional Code. BASIC is a simple, general-purpose language used by people who are not professional programmers.

COBOL stands for Common Business-Oriented Language and, just as the name implies, it is designed especially for business applications.

FORTRAN stands for FORmula TRANslator. FORTRAN is a high-level mathematical-oriented language used primarily for engineering and scientific applications.

RPG stands for Report Program Generator. As the name implies, RPG is a language especially designed for report writing functions.

PASCAL stands for Philips Automatic Sequence Calculator and is a flexible language that can be used interactively as well as for batch processing.

APL stands for A Programming Language. APL is a terminal-oriented language designed especially for interactive problem-solving.

PL/1 stands for Programming Language 1 and is a language designed for both business and scientific applications.

A machine language is one that can be interpreted directly by the electronic circuitry of a computer.

Assembler languages are symbolic languages that are translated by assemblers into a machine language.

WHAT ARE MICROS, MINIS, MAINFRAMES, AND SUPERS?

Computers are categorized according to size of micros, minis, mainframes, and supers. Everyone agrees that these are the categories used, but they disagree on how to actually place computers in these categories. It's a lot like categorizing automobiles as subcompacts, compacts, full-size, and luxury cars. What cars fit into which categories depends on whom you are talking to or, better yet, whom you believe. The same is true of computers.

Some people base the categorization on cost; others base it according to processing speed, memory capacity, or word size. The problem with these methods and all others that might be used is this: computer technology changes so rapidly that almost any criteria established quickly becomes invalid.

For the sake of discussion, let's categorize computers according to word size, processing speed, and memory capacity. Using these factors as the criteria, the smallest computers are micros, next are minis, next are mainframes, and the largest are supers (Figure 1–9). In order to categorize computers in this way, one must know something about word size, processing speed, and memory capacity.

These three criteria are listed separately, but in reality they are intertwined, overlapping factors that go together hand-in-hand. A simple rule of thumb to remember in categorizing computers using these three criteria is **the greater the word size, memory capacity, and processing speed, the larger the computer** (e.g., a minicomputer has a greater word size, memory capacity, and processing speed than a microcomputer). In fact, the larger the word size and memory

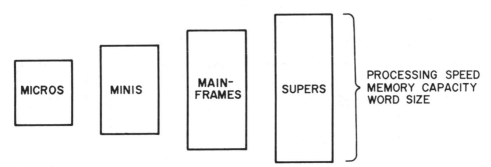

Figure 1–9 *Computer size categories*

capacity are the reasons that the processing speed is greater. For this reason, a supercomputer can process more data faster than a mainframe, which is faster than a mini, which is faster than a micro.

Word Size

This is where the terms "bit" and "byte" enter the picture. **Bit** actually stands for Binary digIT. A binary digit, or bit, is the smallest unit used to represent data in a ditital computer. A **byte** is a certain number of adjacent bits operating as a unit. The actual number of bits in a byte varies according to the computer. However, it is common practice to say that one byte is eight bits.

The main memory of a digital computer, regardless of whether it is a micro, mini, mainframe, or super, is like a series of post office boxes or pigeon-holes. The size of an individual pigeonhole or memory location is the word size of the computer in question.

Memory locations, in the current state of technology, are sized as 8-, 16-, 32-, and 36-bit locations. Of course an 8-bit memory location or word size is smaller than a 16-bit word size.

To understand the significance of word size in categorizing computers, suppose you have 15 pigeonholes such as those in Figure 1–10. If you have an

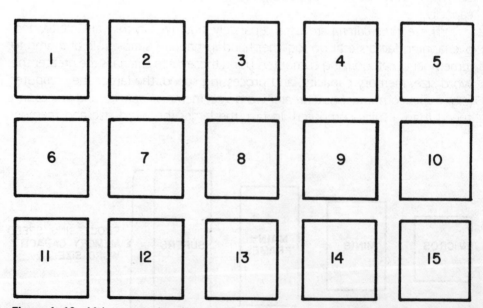

Figure 1–10   Main memory locations

8-bit computer, each hole can hold less than if you have a 16-, 32-, or 36-bit computer. Consequently, the larger the word size, the larger the computer category that the computer fits into.

Memory Capacity

Memory capacity is a function of the number of pigeonholes or memory locations available. It is common practice to state the number of locations in **kilos** or **K**s for simplicity and convenience.

A kilo is typically thought of as representing 1,000. However, in the world of computers, 1 kilo or 1K = 1,024. Consequently, a 256K memory capacity means a capacity of 262,144 locations (256 × 1,024) if the measurement unit is bits. The same 256K would represent 2,097,152 memory locations (256 × 1,024 × 8) if the measurement unit is bytes. Even larger computers might measure the number of memory locations in megabytes. ("Mega" means 1,000,000.)

Processing Speed

Computer time is extremely fast compared to human time. People perform tasks in weeks, days, hours, minutes, and, on occasion, seconds. Computers, on the other hand, perform tasks in milli, micro, and even nanoseconds. (A "millisecond" is one-thousandth of a second. A "microsecond" is one-millionth of a second. A "nanosecond" is one-billionth of a second.)

Processing means to perform various operations on data, such as "read" and "manipulate," according to instructions spelled out in computer programs. Naturally, as a rule, supercomputers can process data faster than mainframes, which can process faster than minis, which can process faster than micros, which can process faster than humans.

Now that you know about word size, memory capacity, and processing speed, it would be nice and neat if I could simply say that any computer that has *X* word size, *Y* memory capacity, and *Z* processing speed is a blank computer. Unfortunately, it's not that simple because advances in technology keep changing the specifications. Categorizing computers according to cost, word size, memory capacity, and processing speed—or any other criteria—is like playing a game in which the rules constantly change. As soon as you think you have a handle on the situation, the rules change and you are back to square one.

At one point in time, any computer with a 16-bit word size would be considered a mini. Now there are 16-bit *and* 32-bit minis. In addition, a 1985 mini might process data faster than a 1980 mainframe.

You don't really need to be able to categorize computers according to the criteria above in order to be literate. Rather, you need to know what the various categories are, their order from smallest (micro) to largest (super), and that a super has a greater word size, memory capacity, and processing speed than a micro.

WHO STARTED THE COMPUTER REVOLUTION?

Some historians would trace the computer revolution all the way back to the year 2000 B.C. with the invention of the abacus. Some trace it back to the arithmetic machine invented by Blaise Pascal in 1647, some to Charles Babbage's machine-driven calculator called the "difference engine" or his more advanced "analytical engine." Others trace the computer revolution to a number of different times and inventions.

Although all of these inventions contributed greatly to the eventual development of what we now know as the computer, in this book we will leave such discussions to the historians. For our purposes, the computer revolution began in 1945 with the invention of the first computer that fits the definition given earlier in this chapter.

This first real electronic computer was known as ENIAC, an acronym for Electronic Numerical Integrator and Calculator. It did not store programs, so ENIAC did violate one of the four characteristics set forth earlier.

The first computer to store programs was EDSAC, an acronym for Electronic Delay Storage Automatic Computer, which was invented in 1949.

A major breakthrough in the computer revolution occurred in 1951 when the Sperry Rand Corporation built the famous UNIVAC 1 computer—the Universal Automatic Computer. UNIVAC 1 became the first computer to be used commercially when it was purchased by the federal government's Census Bureau.

By today's standards, UNIVAC 1 would be considered an oversized bucket of nuts, bolts, and vacuum tubes that was extremely limited. However, its invention and commercial use are considered so significant by historians that many claim Sperry Rand and UNIVAC 1 started the computer revolution as we know it today. In fact, tourists may see UNIVAC 1 in the Smithsonian Institute in Washington, D.C., preserved for posterity.

Computers have come a long way since the vacuum tube monsters of UNIVAC 1's time. Storage tube computers are considered the first generation of computers. This generation lasted until 1959 when it was replaced by the smaller, more efficient second generation of computers. The second generation of computers was based on the transistor.

If you are at least 30 years old, you can remember the transistor revolution. It seemed that, overnight, televisions and radios shrank from huge console models to small portables. The transistor radio and portable television became commonplace. The transistor had the same impact on computers. Transistors allowed computers to simultaneously become smaller, faster, and capable of storing greater amounts of data. It was during the second generation of computers (1959–1965) that the computer revolution really began to escalate.

But if the transistors put the computer revolution in gear, a third-generation invention—the integrated circuit—put it in overdrive! The integrated circuit (IC) allowed thousands of electronic components to be miniaturized and placed on silicon wafers or **chips** no larger than a child's fingernail. Again, computers became simultaneously smaller, faster, and capable of storing more data. The third generation of computers (1965–1970) has given way to the fourth generation, and the development continues.

Rapid, constant developments in the field of microelectronics continue to make computers smaller, faster, more powerful, more flexible, and able to store greater amounts of data. The explosion of computer developments and use that has taken place in the fourth generation has resulted in lower prices. Lower prices have resulted in broader acceptance and use. This, in turn, has brought more and more people into the business of developing computer software. The combination of less-expensive, more-capable hardware and less-expensive, more-capable software has broadened the number of computer applications exponentially.

IS THERE ANYBODY LEFT WHO DOESN'T USE A COMPUTER?

An interesting exercise is to try to identify an occupation that is not at least indirectly affected by the computer. Computers are used by the military and in the fields of medicine, law, education, transportation, construction, manufacturing, sales, business, entertainment, and leisure—virtually every form of human endeavor, including, of course, design and drafting.

Thanks to the computer, you can conduct business at many banks 24 hours a day. Your local auto mechanic uses computer diagnosis to identify your car's problems and then uses a computer to produce the bill. Checkout at grocery stores has been simplified by computers, as have inventory, ordering, and stocking goods. Electric typewriters are being replaced by word processors, which are nothing more than computers especially adapted for secretarial tasks. Spend time in a hospital and you will become intimately involved with computers from admissions to checkout and billing. It is safe to say that the everyday operations of the public and private sectors in this country depend on the computer.

A good way to come to appreciate the impact of computers on everyday commerce and interaction is to select a day and keep a log of your activities. Record in the log each time you come in contact, either directly or indirectly, with a computer. All in all, as a society, we have benefitted immensely from the computer revolution. However, it has introduced several critical issues with which you should be familiar.

IF COMPUTERS ARE SO GOOD, WHAT'S ALL THE FUSS ABOUT?

You open your electric bill and it says you owe $1,000,000! You wait in line for an hour at the airline ticket counter only to find you don't have a reservation. You register for a college leisure class in art and wind up in a calculus class. You are stopped for a speeding ticket and then arrested under the name of a person you've never heard of.

All of these are actual examples of situations that have occurred and continue to occur in the modern world of computers. Such mistakes have given us a whole new class of excuses—computer error. We've probably all been told, "I'm sorry, the computer made a mistake." Although most so-called computer errors are actually the mistakes of people who operate computers, the fact remains that the computer has unlocked a Pandora's box of new problems.

Computers and legal experts are struggling with the information revolution that is actually an offshoot of the computer revolution. The problem is the relatively easy access to information that computers give us weighed against the individual's right to privacy. This is a critical issue because there is little about a person's life that is not stored in a computer somewhere. And anyone who has access to the data or who knows how to gain access has access to the most private of information about individuals. If you have even one credit card—and who doesn't—mountains of financial and personal data about you are readily available to numerous people whom you don't even know.

Computer crime is becoming a serious problem. By gaining access to a bank's computer system, a computer criminal can transfer the funds from your account to his by simply pressing buttons. Cases of computer crime are beginning to be heard about almost daily. By now we are all familiar with the scenario in which a computer "hacker" gains access to the military's computers that control nuclear missiles. In another example, an employee of a large university sells degrees to people who never attended the university through computer trickery.

Another issue of concern is dependency. In the smallest sense, this is seen in a young person who cannot perform basic mathematical operations without the aid of a calculator. In its largest sense, it is a nation's economy or defense systems that cannot function without computers. Many people believe that modern society is becoming too dependent on computers.

Yet another issue of concern, the one most important to design and drafting personnel, is the "machine-replaces-man" syndrome. There is no question that the increased productivity brought about by computers means that many jobs are being eliminated by computers and other forms of computer-based automation such as robots. Society must find an answer to the question: "What can we do with and for workers who are displaced by computer technology?" Computers simply are not creating as many new jobs as they are displacing.

These are issues that must be dealt with. To you, however, the most important issue is how the computer is affecting the world of design and drafting. Now that you are computer-literate, you are prepared to take up this issue.

Chapter 2
DESIGN AND DRAFTING:
FROM T-SQUARES TO COMPUTERS

Chapter 1 helped you develop the foundation of computer knowledge necessary to understand computer-aided design and drafting, hereafter referred to as CADD. This chapter will build on the foundation the beginnings of an understanding of CADD. Chapter 2 will answer the following questions:

1. What is design?
2. What is drafting?
3. How did design and drafting evolve?
4. What is CADD?
5. How does CADD compare to manual drafting?
6. What are the advantages of CADD?
7. What are some modern CADD applications?
8. What is the social impact of CADD?

WHAT IS DESIGN?

An understanding of computer-aided design and drafting begins with an understanding of plain design and drafting. Design is the process whereby creative, analytic, and scientific principles are brought together and focused on meeting a need or solving a problem. Design is the foundation of both the manufacturing and construction industries. Before any product can be manufactured, it must be designed. Before a structure can be built, it must be designed.

Designers must bridge the gap between function and aesthetics. In other words, any product that is designed must look good *and* work. This is what makes design such an interesting and challenging process. As a process, design can be considered both an art and a science.

It is important to understand the marriage of function and aesthetics in design because it is one of the reasons behind the development of CADD. Designers since Leonardo Da Vinci have sought tools and techniques to help improve their ability and productivity in designing for both function and aesthetics. CADD represents a quantum leap in this regard.

To appreciate the difficulty a designer faces in trying to treat both function and aesthetics, consider these examples from everyday life. For the purpose of this illustration, women go first. Think back to the last time you had to dress up for a formal occasion. You shopped for hours until you found just the right dress. But when trying it on, you found that in spite of its gorgeous appearance, it wasn't comfortable. The designer did a good job with regard to aesthetics but a poor job with regard to function. Consequently, you looked good for your big night out but were uncomfortable the whole time.

Now let's look at the men's side. Nearly everyone agrees that men look good in tuxedos, but the person who invented the tux should be forced to wear one forever! Trying to get comfortable in a cumerbund and a bow tie is like trying to sleep on a bed of nails. This is another example of good aesthetics but poor functional design.

Now let's consider the opposite problem. Some designs are functionally sound but aesthetically lacking. In other words, they work well but don't look very good. An example of such design is the old "Willy's" jeep that used to be the standard mode of transportation in the U.S. Army. This little jeep worked well and was popular with the troops, but it never won any car-of-the-year awards for beauty in design.

In some design situations, aesthetics takes precedence over function, and the opposite is true in other cases. However, in most cases both function and aesthetics are important. In these design situations, regardless of whether the product is a car, a house, a computer, a machine part, or a printed circuit board, the design process is basically the same. It is a systematic, five-step process used to meet needs or solve problems, as shown in Figure 2–1.

A good way to illustrate the various steps in the design process is to use the example of a house. You may not be interested in architectural drafting, but a house is something we can all relate to regardless of our varied backgrounds and work settings. The first step begins when someone decides to have a house built. The house, then, is the need or design problem.

Step 1 is problem **identification**. In this step, designers clearly identify the problem and make sure that all parties know what the problem is. In the example, this would involve working with the person who wants the house built (the buyer) to develop a list of needs which will clearly delineate the problem (e.g., What size of house? What style? How many bedrooms? Garage or carport? Open or closed design?). With the problem clearly identified, designers move on to Step 2.

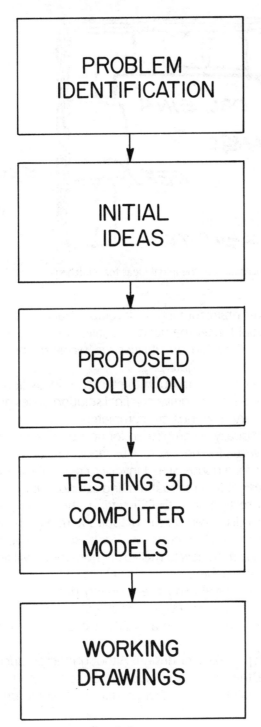

Figure 2–1   The design process

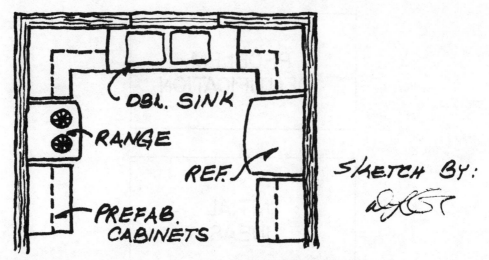

Figure 2–2   Documentation of the initial ideas for a kitchen

Step 2 involves **brainstorming** to develop initial ideas. There are hundreds of designs that would meet the needs identified in Step 1. In Step 2, no good idea is ruled out. All design possibilities are recorded through sketches and notes, such as the one in Figure 2–2.

In Step 3, designers sift through the tentative ideas developed in the previous step with the buyer and arrive at a **final solution** or design for the house. At this point, preliminary drawings are completed.

Step 4 is not usually accomplished for houses, but it is for larger construction projects. However, for the sake of illustration, presume that Step 4 is part of the design process for a house. Step 4 involves creating a **model** or **prototype** of the preliminary design. In a manual drafting setting, the model would be built by the modelling section. In a CADD setting, the model would be a three-dimensional model displayed on the graphics terminal. The model allows the buyer to actually see what the house will look like before accepting the design as final. It also allows designers to make sure everything will fit together and the design will work as planned.

Step 5 involves **developing the working drawings** for the design. The drawings will incorporate any revisions decided on in Step 4. The finished working drawings, if accomplished on a CADD system, might look like the one in Figure 2–3.

These five steps represent design. Although the product designed in this case was a house, the same system would be used if it had been a car, a boat, an electronic calculator, or any other product that would be manufactured or built.

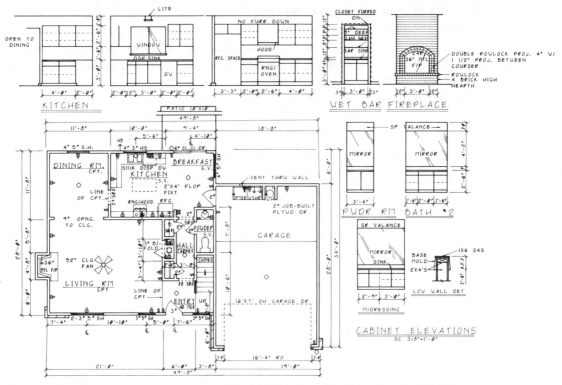

Figure 2–3 Floor plan produced on a modern CADD system *(Courtesy Bausch & Lomb)*

Now it's time to look at drafting. Although the two terms are used together a great deal—so much so, in fact, that they have become synonymous—they are not the same thing. In order to understand CADD, you must know the difference.

WHAT IS DRAFTING?

This probably seems a rather simplistic question to most readers. However, many people who have been in drafting for years are not able to answer this question clearly and concisely. If asked to define drafting, most people say something about drawing plans. And although drafting does involve drawing plans, this response does not completely define drafting as a process or an occupation. However, if you understand the design process as just set forth, there is a very simple, all-encompassing definition for drafting that works well: **Drafting is the process through which design is documented.** Said another way, drafting is documenting the design process.

This definition of drafting not only ties design and drafting together as a good definition should, but it makes the important distinction between the two processes and covers the many tasks which are accomplished under the collective heading of "drafting." These tasks include completing sketches, preliminary drawings, and working drawings; tracking bills of material, parts lists, and schedules; making notes, legends, and specifications; and recording calculations.

Producing any visual product that is needed to *document* the design process falls under the heading of drafting. In Step 1 of the design process, sketches and notes may be needed to document the definition of the problem. In Step 2, sketches, notes, and calculations may be needed to document initial ideas for the design. In Step 3, preliminary drawings are produced to document the proposed solution. In Step 4, a three-dimensional computer model or a manually built model is used to document the proposed solution in a form that can be understood by laypeople and tested by experts. Step 5 is what most people associate with drafting. But as you can see, it's not the only phase of the design process that involves drafting. The working drawings produced in this phase document the final design and communicate it to the various tradespeople who will be involved in the conversion process.

Now that you understand design and drafting as two related but separate concepts, you are ready to see how they developed from where they have been in the past to where they are today—CADD.

HOW DID DESIGN AND DRAFTING EVOLVE?

The design process itself has not changed a great deal over the years. Different people have different names for each of the five steps. Some people even add or subtract a step, but all of the different names boil down to the same process that has been used for centuries. The only real change in the design process over the years has been in the way the various steps are accomplished. For example, three-dimensional computer models have now replaced scale models or prototypes in those companies that have been converted to CADD. Step 4 still requires models, but they are produced differently.

Unlike the design process, drafting has changed a great deal over the years, and the changes are visually apparent—they can be easily seen. There have been many time- and work-saving developments in drafting. CADD is nothing more than the latest, albeit the most significant, in a long list of developments that have come about to make the drafter more productive. Drafting is still what it has always been: documenting the design process. However, the tools and techniques used for drafting have changed considerably with the advent of CADD.

The differences in the drafting tools are easy to see. Figure 2–4 shows the types of tools and devices used for drafting manually. Figures 2–5 and 2–6 show the comparable tools in a CADD setting.

A drafter in the 1960s used a T-square, pencils, triangles, scales, tape, dry cleaning pads, erasers, erasing shields, dividers, a bow compass, and an assortment of other manual tools. The tools of a modern drafter are a keyboard, a graphics terminal, a tablet, menus, light pens or pucks, and a plotter.

Between the two extremes illustrated in Figures 2–4, 2–5, and 2–6, numerous other changes developed on the way to CADD. T-squares were replaced by parallel bars, which in time were replaced by drafting machines. Mechanical pencils, electric erasers, templates, and dry transfer sheets were all significant developments. Such processes as pin-registered overlay drafting, scissors drafting, and photodrafting were also important developments. But the most significant development in the history of drafting is CADD.

The first CADD system to be sold commercially was made available by IBM in 1964. The first stand-alone or "turnkey" CADD system on the market was produced by Applicon Incorporated. (Both IBM and Applicon are still leaders in CADD, as you will see in later chapters.) Although the CADD revolution officially began in 1964, it did not really take off until 1980. By 1980, CADD systems were being manufactured and marketed by almost 100 companies for a wide variety of applications.

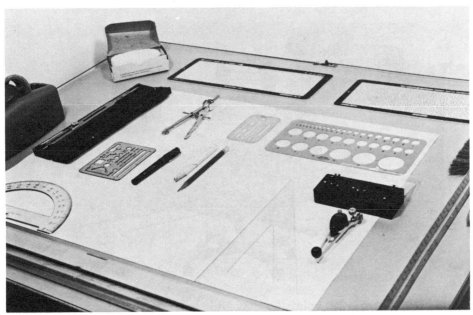

Figure 2–4 Manual drafting tools *(Courtesy Deborah M. Goetsch)*

Figure 2–5 Modern CADD system (Courtesy Bausch & Lomb)

Figure 2–6 Modern CADD system (Courtesy PSI Systems Corporation)

We've talked around the term long enough. It's time to find out what CADD really is.

WHAT IS CADD?

CADD is the acronym for Computer-Aided Design and Drafting. Computer-aided design means using the computer and peripheral devices as tools in accomplishing the five steps in the design process. Computer-aided drafting means using the computer and peripheral devices in documenting the design process. Consequently, computer-aided design and drafting (CADD) means using the computer and peripheral devices to accomplish and document the design process.

The acronym CADD was devised to put a minor controversy to rest. That controversy centered around the question, "Does CADD mean computer-aided design or computer-aided drafting?" The answer has always depended on the intentions of the person using the term. Historically speaking, CAD was first used to mean computer-aided design. When this was common terminology, the equivalent term for drafting was AD (Automated Drafting). AD did not catch on, and soon CAD was being used interchangeably to mean either computer-aided design or computer-aided drafting.

This interchange led to confusion because certain CAD systems were designed and marketed as design systems while others were primarily drafting-oriented systems. Matters were further complicated when systems that could easily handle both design and drafting tasks began to reach the market. The differences, of course, were in the software available. Design software needed capabilities such as geometric modelling, finite analysis, and, in some cases, simulation or even animation. The software for drafting applications could be considerably less complex, consisting primarily of two-dimensional geometric building blocks, alphanumerics, and relatively simple manipulation and modification functions. Most drafting systems that claimed to have "3-D" capabilities were usually limited to "wireframe" 3-D.

As CAD technology advanced, systems began to appear on the market that could both design and draft and could treat both processes in depth. This eventually led to the compromise term CADD.

There are several CADD-related terms with which you should also be familiar. The most frequently heard terms are computer graphics, interactive graphics, CAM, CAI, and CAD/CAM.

Computer graphics is an umbrella term that encompasses the many ways computers can be used to produce graphics. These applications range from simple charts and graphs, to working drawings, to animated cartoons, to movies. CADD is one form of computer graphics.

Interactive graphics is another term heard frequently. It is a term that, like CADD, grew out of the computer revolution. Graphics, of course, has to do with data that consist of points, lines, and planes (2-D and 3-D pictures). Interactive means a two-way processing of data in which a human can redirect the processing by direct intervention with the computer. Interactive graphics means interacting with a computer to redirect the processing of graphic data.

CADD, of course, involves interactive graphics. If a user of a CADD system creates a drawing and displays it on the graphics terminal, the user is involved in interactive graphics every time some aspect of the drawing is manipulated, modified, or otherwise directly interacted with through the keyboard or any other cursor control or input device.

CAM and **CAI** are manufacturing terms that grew out of the computer revolution. CAM is the acronym for computer-aided manufacturing. As the name implies, CAM is the use of computers in any phase or aspect of the manufacturing process. CAI is the acronym for computer-aided inspection. CAI involves using the computer in support of the quality control process in manufacturing.

CAD/CAM means computer-aided design/computer-aided manufacturing. When these concepts are successfully and fully married, the result is the ultimate in productivity improvement in a manufacturing setting. CAD/CAM involves electronically linking the design and manufacturing components. In a true CAD/CAM situation, the data base that is created during the design process is used in producing the instructions that will guide the automated manufacturing processes.

HOW DOES CADD COMPARE TO MANUAL DRAFTING?

In most cases when the conversation is about CADD versus manual drafting, talk centers around productivity ratios. Be very careful about the productivity ratios you hear quoted; none of them are fixed. Productivity ratios can vary drastically for different CADD systems, different settings, different applications, and different users. There are simply too many variables involved to accept the productivity gains of another user as being typical of what you can expect to gain from CADD. In the final analysis, the same CADD system in the same types of applications will yield drastically different results, depending on the skills and creativity of the people who use the system.

You should be doubly careful of individual task comparisons. A perfect example to beware of is one of the favorites of people who enjoy making these comparisons. It involves comparing manual lettering with lettering on a CADD system. Naturally, a person who can type well will be able to create text on a

CADD system much faster than it could be lettered freehand. A ratio of 50:1 would not be unrealistic in such a comparison. However, such comparisons do not tell the whole story, and in the past they have caused people to become disenchanted with CADD when the 50:1 productivity gains were not accomplished after converting.

It takes time and experience to really learn how much more productive a design and drafting operation has become after a conversion from manual techniques to CADD. In most applications, 2:1, 3:1, or even 4:1 productivity gains can be expected once a complete conversion has been accomplished. The gains will have a tendency to start low or even fall behind the productivity that was being achieved during the manual operation. This is because drafters who are experts manually are rookies again when it comes to CADD. However, as their skills in working with CADD grow, so do the productivity gains.

One way to get a realistic comparison of manual drafting and CADD is to define several design and drafting tasks and to compare them side by side, accomplished manually and with CADD.

Typical Design Tasks

Three tasks must be performed on every design project, regardless of the nature of the project and whether the design process will be undertaken manually or with the help of CADD: modelling, analysis, and review. These three tasks can be easily compared in CADD versus manual test studies.

Modelling. The differences between computer modelling and manual modelling have already been described in general terms. Computer models are developed and displayed on the graphics terminal of a CADD system. Developing a three-dimensional computer model involves entering three types of commands:

1. Geometric construction commands (e.g., points, lines, rectangles, circles, ellipses)
2. Manipulation commands (e.g., scale, rotate, move, zoom in)
3. Joining commands (join the two-dimensional elements together to make a three-dimensional model)

By contrast, to build a live scale model manually requires such tasks as:

1. Obtaining preliminary drawings
2. Collecting all of the required building materials
3. Cutting materials to the specified sizes and shapes
4. Manually putting the model together piece by piece

The differences in time required to build computer models as compared to live scale models will vary greatly, depending on the individual situation. However, in any case it takes considerably longer to build live models. For the purpose of comparison, a modelling test was conducted in the design and drafting program of Okaloosa-Walton Junior College. In this comparison study, a live model that took 42 hours to complete was accomplished in 8 hours on a CADD system. The model subject was a one-story ranch-style house.

Analysis. Analysis is one of the strengths of CADD. Special programs are available for the various types of analytic calculations, such as load, stress, friction, and heat transfer, that might be required in a design project. If a CADD system has the proper software, a user can input the variables and have a complete analysis in seconds.

On the other hand, even with electronic calculators, analysis can be a time-consuming process. In another experiment conducted in the drafting and design program at Okaloosa-Walton Junior College, a simple load analysis that took 2 minutes on a CADD system took 4 hours to accomplish manually.

Review. Several CADD features have significantly simplified the review process in design. Dimensioning errors have been reduced by the automatic dimensioning feature of most CADD systems. The zoom-in feature allows designers to move in close or blow up intricate details for a closer look at such things as tolerances, fits, and interferences. Probably the most valuable CADD feature with regard to review is layering.

A CADD system will allow a designer to separate a design into various layers and overlay them in different colors for review. An example in which layering might be used in the design process can be found in a typical architectural drafting problem—the design of an HVAC (heating-ventilation-air conditioning) system for a house or building. The floor plan for the house can be prepared on one layer in a color—say, red. The HVAC layout can be prepared on another layer in another color—say, blue. To review the HVAC layout for accuracy, proper coverage, and interference, the HVAC layout is superimposed over the floor plan layer. The designer can readily see if any rooms have been missed or if any interferences exist.

Manual review, by comparison, is time consuming. The differences between the two processes with regard to time can be illustrated with a simple example. Suppose a late revision causes a critical dimension to be changed in a set of plans. The automatic dimensioning feature of most CADD systems will follow through, make the dimensional change everywhere it should occur, and make any corresponding dimensional changes. To do the same task manually would mean that the entire set of plans would have to be scrutinized closely to determine all of the different places the dimensional change would be required and what other changes it would cause. When this has been done, the changes must be calculated, made, and checked. A task that could be accomplished in seconds on most CADD systems would take hours to achieve manually.

Typical Drafting Tasks

Two tasks must be performed on every drafting project, whether the mode is manual or CADD. These tasks are lettering and linework. They can be easily compared in CADD versus manual drafting test studies.

In manual drafting, lettering is accomplished freehand with the assistance of guidelines from a lettering guide. Freehand lettering is a slow process. In CADD, lettering is accomplished by typing. Even if a user "hunts and pecks" using one finger, he or she will be able to type faster than another drafter could letter freehand. If users are good or even fair typists, their lettering on a CADD system will surpass even the best freehand letterer. A ratio of 50:1 would be easily accomplished. However, such a comparison taken out of context is meaningless, since drafting projects involve much more than just lettering.

Linework is accomplished in manual drafting using mechanical pencils and a drafting machine. Even with the most modern manual tools, linework is a slow, arduous task. Linework is accomplished on a CADD system by selecting the appropriate geometric commands from a menu and manipulating the cursor. Geometric characters such as lines, points, circles, rectangles, triangles, and polygons can be produced in seconds on a CADD system.

Figures 2–7 and 2–8 are construction details that were used as the subjects of an experiment conducted in the drafting and design program at Okaloosa-Walton Junior College. Figure 2–7 is a foundation detail for a brick veneer on a frame house that was prepared on a microcomputer-based CADD system. From the beginning of its development until the completion of plotting, this detail took 18 minutes. To prepare the same detail manually in pencil took a skilled drafter 38 minutes. To prepare the same detail in ink took the same drafter 1 hour and 12 minutes. It should be noted that the microcomputer-based CADD system used in this experiment is considered much slower than most CADD systems.

Figure 2–8 is a foundation detail for a house with a 4-inch slab-on-grade floor system that was prepared on the same microcomputer-based CADD system as Figure 2–7. Beginning of development to completion of plotting took 16 minutes. To prepare the same detail manually in pencil took a skilled drafter 36 minutes; in ink it took 1 hour and 9 minutes.

These actual examples show that CADD compares favorably with manual drafting in terms of productivity. And whatever the productivity ratios are today, they will only improve in favor of CADD. However, do not forget that the actual productivity gains accomplished will depend on:

1. The application area (architectural, electronic, mechanical)
2. The CADD system(s) used

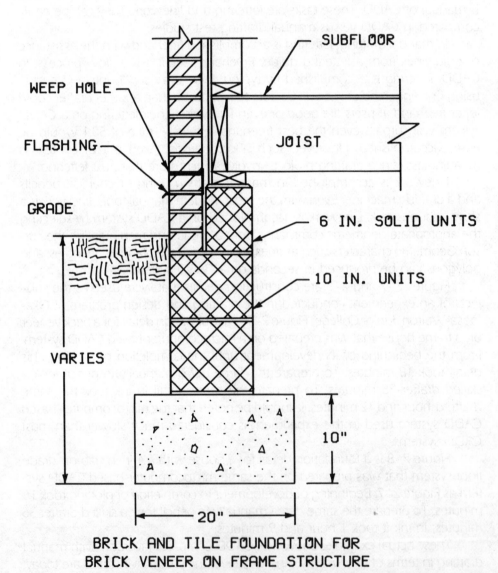

BRICK AND TILE FOUNDATION FOR
BRICK VENEER ON FRAME STRUCTURE

Figure 2–7 Foundation detail produced on a microcomputer-based CADD system

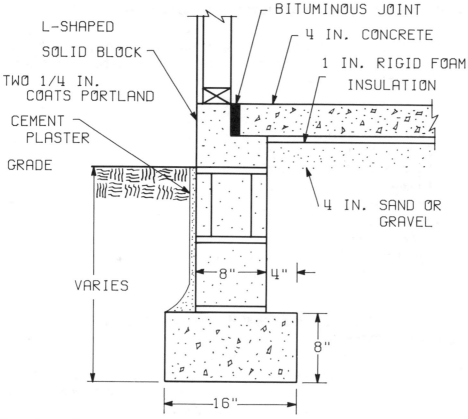

Figure 2–8 Foundation detail produced on a microcomputer-based CADD system

3. The skills, experience, and creativity of the users
4. The acceptance of CADD at all levels within the company

Many companies that manufacture and market CADD systems include proclamations of 3:1, 5:1, and 12:1 productivity ratios in their marketing brochures. Although these figures are no doubt valid, they mean very little unless you know all of the variables involved in arriving at them. They may be valid ratios for one company but not for yours.

The only valid ratio for you is the one determined in your individual work setting using your variables. Some manufacturers are willing to help you run test trials such as those described earlier in this chapter using actual projects from your company. If you undertake such comparisons, be sure to select tasks that are intrinsic to your application area and for which you have accurate data on manual operations.

WHAT ARE THE ADVANTAGES OF CADD?

CADD offers a number of advantages over manual design and drafting. The one dealt with above, of course, is improved productivity, and it is important. However, there are several other advantages that you should be aware of:

Faster, less-expensive modelling
Faster, more-accurate analysis
Easier, more-reliable review
Faster drafting
Neater drafting
More consistent drafting
More accurate drafting
Simplified and faster revisions and corrections
Easier storage requiring less space

WHAT ARE SOME MODERN CADD SYSTEM APPLICATIONS?

There are numerous types of drafting. Each type is known as an **application**. Most drafters are employed in situations that relate directly or indirectly to the construction or the manufacturing industries.

The use of CADD in a given application is limited only by the software available for that application. And software is readily available for every common drafting application. In addition, general-purpose software is available for use in any drafting application.

CADD is being used in all of the following construction-related applications and more:

Architectural design
Architectural drafting
Landscape design
Landscape drafting
Structural engineering
Structural drafting
Electrical design
Electrical drafting
HVAC and plumbing design
HVAC and plumbing drafting

Interior design
Interior design drafting
Civil engineering
Civil engineering/survey drafting

CADD is also being used in the following manufacturing-related applications:

Mechanical engineering
Mechanical drafting
Printed circuit board design
Printed circuit board drafting
Industrial engineering and plant layout
Quality control
Jig and fixture design
Jig and fixture drafting

In addition to these common design and drafting applications, CADD is being used in numerous other less-common applications, such as facility planning and education/training.

WHAT IS THE SOCIAL IMPACT OF CADD?

In spite of the many advantages it offers, CADD is not without its detractors. CADD represents change—significant change. It alters extensively and forever the way design and drafting are accomplished. Many experienced designers and drafters are reluctant to accept CADD, feeling they will be replaced by a computer.

Although CADD systems will not take the place of designers and drafters in the work force, they will allow fewer designers and drafters to accomplish even more work in less time. Consequently, in the long run the number of designers and drafters needed at a given company may decline. How much of a decline that can be expected by the turn of the century is still anybody's guess, but at some point in time a downturn should be noticed. Consequently, one social impact of CADD is fear of displacement. How to effectively deal with such fears is covered in a later chapter.

Another social factor to consider with CADD is the fear of the unknown it generates. CADD is new, and many people have a natural distrust or fear of anything new. Both fear of change and fear of the unknown can have an impact on the success of a company's CADD conversion. Whether or not a conversion to CADD is ultimately successful depends on the people involved in the conversion. This is another social factor to consider. Even the best hardware and software on the market are of little value without skilled users who accept the change CADD represents and are willing to be creative in finding ways to make it a productive venture.

Drafting and design managers planning a CADD conversion should be aware of the social implications and have a plan for dealing with them. How to develop such a plan is covered in Chapter 7 on implementation. Sales personnel planning to market CADD technology should also be aware of the social implications and how they can impact the relationship after the sale.

Unfortunately, the social aspects of CADD have been mostly neglected by those responsible for research and development. Since the early days of CADD, millions of dollars have been spent on the development, production, and marketing of CADD technology. In comparison, very little has been spent in the area of people development with regard to CADD.

Most research in the private sector and the academic community has focused on developing better hardware and software. Most training provided for users is of a how-to nature. The greatest unexplored area with regard to CADD involves identifying and overcoming the possible negative social implications. Any such effort will require a joint effort of companies that manufacture and market CADD technology, companies that use it, and educational institutions involved in CADD-related training and research.

Chapter 3
THE CADD SYSTEM

The term "CADD system" is used a great deal these days, and often loosely. Most people look at a collection of hardward and call it a system. This is acceptable practice for everyday conversation. In fact, for the purpose of convenience and simplicity, it is even recommended. However, a person who is knowledgeable about CADD must understand that a specially configured collection of hardware is properly referred to as a hardware configuration. A true CADD system has three components:

1. Hardware
2. Software
3. Users

This chapter will answer the following questions about CADD systems:

1. What are the various items of hardware found in a typical configuration?
2. What are the types of software used in CADD?
3. What kinds of users are associated with CADD?

Hardware is an umbrella term used when talking about the machines and devices in a CADD system. When you look at a CADD system, you are looking at hardware. *Software* is the umbrella term for all of the computer programs and supporting documentation associated with CADD. *Users* are the people who use the CADD system to accomplish design and drafting tasks. It takes all three components to have a CADD system.

CADD HARDWARE

The hardware in a CADD hardware configuration can be divided into the following categories: the processor and secondary storage units; input and cursor control devices; and output devices. Thinking back to Chapter 1, you will

Figure 3–1   Modern CADD hardware configuration *(Courtesy Bausch & Lomb)*

recall that a computer system consists of a computer and various peripheral devices. The same is true of a CADD system. The computer in a CADD system is the processor. The secondary storage units, input and cursor control devices, and output devices are the peripherals.

In a typical CADD configuration, secondary storage units are disk or tape drives. Input and cursor control devices include the keyboard, a digitizer, a graphics tablet with puck or light pen, and various miscellaneous cursor control device options such as thumbwheels, joysticks, and trackballs. Output devices consist of plotters, printers, graphics terminals, and text terminals.

Figure 3–1 is an example of a modern CADD hardware configuration. The components from left to right are pen plotter; processor and disk drive unit; graphics display with keyboard and thumbwheels; tablet with light pen; text display with keyboard; and digitizer with multibutton puck.

The Processor and Disk Drive Unit

The processor is the computer in a CADD system. Processors in a CADD system range from 8-bit to 36-bit processors that are packaged in a variety of ways. In some systems, the processor is housed in a console that also contains the graphics display and keyboard (Figure 3–2). Other processors are housed in stand-alone console units into which the CADD work stations are interfaced (Figure 3–3).

Figure 3–2 Processor housed in console below the terminal *(Courtesy Bausch & Lomb)*

Figure 3–3 Stand-alone processor with disk drive unit (right) *(Courtesy Bausch & Lomb)*

Regardless of a processor's size or packaging, there are certain applicable processor-related terms with which you should be familiar, including memory mapping, cache memory, virtual memory, on-line storage, and off-line storage.

Memory mapping is a concept that is used to reduce the amount of time required to locate and retrieve any data stored in the main memory of the processor. If you were sent to the post office to retrieve the mail for five friends but were not given their box numbers, you would face the same problem a computer faces when it must retrieve data from storage. You walk into the post office to find there are 500 boxes. With the information you have, all you can do is search through every box and retrieve anything with your friends' names on it. Memory mapping is a method that directs the computer right to specific memory locations when it is searching for data. This allows it to go straight to the desired data, thereby cutting down on search time and protecting data in the other locations.

Cache memory is a concept used to speed interaction between the main memory and processing sections of a CADD system's processor. A cache memory is a small extra memory into which frequently used data are stored. It's like having a small auxiliary toolbox in which you store the tools you use most. That way when they are needed, they are easier to find. Frequently used data in a CADD system may be stored in cache memory to reduce the amount of time required to find data in the main memory, retrieve it, and move it to the processing section.

Virtual memory is a concept that allows extremely long programs to be broken up into sections. The section of the program to be used is immediately housed in the virtual memory, which is a specially partitioned-off section of memory. The remainder of the long program is stored on a secondary storage device (disk or tape). When another section of the program is needed, it is placed into the virtual memory and replaces the preceding piece, which is then stored on disk or tape. Virtual memory prevents excessively large programs from filling all of the main memory space and not leaving any room for other input and interaction.

On-line storage is storage which is immediately available to the user. In other words, on-line storage is the main memory and cache memory when one is used. Sometimes there is discussion as to what actually constitutes on-line storage. The debate centers around a functioning definition for the phrase "immediately available storage." A good rule of thumb to follow in this debate is: on-line storage should be able to yield data for processing in milliseconds.

Off-line storage is storage which is not immediately available or from which data are not immediately available for retrieval and use. Off-line storage is not limited in its capacity as is on-line storage. Since it consists of disks or tapes, there can be an infinite amount of off-line storage.

The Display Terminals (Graphics and Text)

The output of softcopy is accomplished on graphics and text terminals in a CADD system. **Softcopy** is any form of data display that disappears when the CADD system is turned off. Text displays are simple, television-like devices used in some configurations for displaying prompts and other instructional messages for users. Many systems use graphics displays which serve this function as well as display graphic data.

Graphics displays for CADD systems come in monochrome, gray, and color options. Monochrome displays make use of the familiar green phosphor lines on a darker green background. Gray displays use light gray lines on a dark background or dark gray lines on a light gray background. Color displays can display graphic and alphanumeric data in over 200 different colors.

There are three basic types of graphics displays, all of which come in monochrome, gray, and color options, depending on the manufacturer.

Refresh Displays. Refresh graphics displays create graphic and alphanumeric data by directing an electron beam against the back of the display screen. The electron beam in essence draws the image on the back of the screen. Such an image has a very short life and must be constantly redrawn by the beam or it will begin to flicker and lose its form. This constant redrawing is called "refreshing the image," hence the name "refresh display."

Raster Display. Raster displays have become the most popular type of display for use in the graphics terminals of CADD systems. Raster displays create images by illuminating picture elements on the screen. These picture elements are referred to as **pixels**. The more pixels available to illuminate, the better the quality of the picture. This measure of quality of the graphic image is known as **resolution**. A high-resolution image is smooth and clear. A low-resolution image is jagged and poorly defined.

The resolution of a raster display is readily apparent in shapes such as circles, ellipses, and arcs. Since these geometric shapes are created using straight lines, it takes a very-high-resolution display to create them with lines that are so short the circles, ellipses, and arcs do not appear jagged and distorted. There is no hard-and-fast rule governing the line between high and low resolution. However, a good rule of thumb is that a display with over 1,000 columns and 1,000 rows of pixels can be considered a high-resolution display. Raster displays with 1,200 × 1,200 resolution are not uncommon in modern CADD systems. However, some of the low-end microcomputer-based CADD systems have displays with 250 × 300 resolution. In these cases, a circle looks approximately like a stop sign.

Storage Displays. Storage displays are very much like refresh displays, except that the image does not have to be constantly redrawn. Rather, the image, once drawn, is stored. Storage displays can display data in two modes: temporary and permanent. This dual storage and display capability gives users time-saving advantages when activating commands such as ERASE, MOVE, and COPY.

On some displays, each time one of these modification or manipulation commands is activated, the graphics display goes blank and must be repainted. Storage displays allow users to store work temporarily that is being interacted with. Work that is final and correct can be stored in permanent storage. When one of the above commands is given, only those data in temporary storage are affected. Consequently, the user does not have to wait long for the image to be repainted. Once data are correct, they can be moved from temporary storage to permanent storage. Storage displays are not yet used as frequently as rasters in configuring CADD systems, but they are gaining popularity.

You will often hear the terms "graphics display" and "graphics terminal." The **display** is the screen unit on which the image is projected. The **terminal** is the console, the display, and any other built-in features. Figures 3–4 and 3–5 are examples of graphics display options for a modern CADD system.

Figure 3–4   Single graphics display *(Courtesy Bausch & Lomb)*

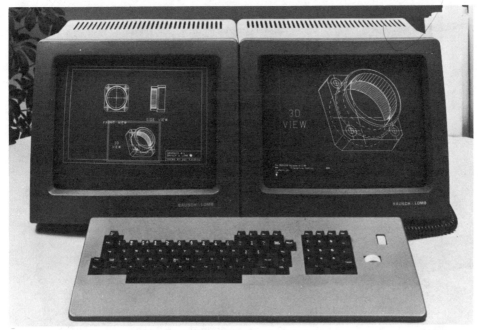

Figure 3–5   Dual graphics display *(Courtesy Bausch & Lomb)*

The Keyboard

The keyboard is one of the primary input devices used with all CADD systems. It may be used for activating CADD commands; entering alphanumeric data, such as notes, on drawings; and locating the cursor or graphic data using coordinates.

A typical keyboard for a CADD system has regular typewriter keys and special-purpose or auxiliary keys. Separate numeric pads and thumbwheels for cursor manipulation are also found on some keyboards.

Figure 3–6 is an example of a keyboard for a modern CADD system. It contains the normal alphanumeric keys, numerous auxiliary keys, a separate set of special function keys, and horizontal and vertical thumbwheels.

The Digitizer

CADD systems are built around digital computers, which you learned about in Chapter 1. You will recall that digital computers can accept only digital data or data which is entered in binary form. This means there must be a special

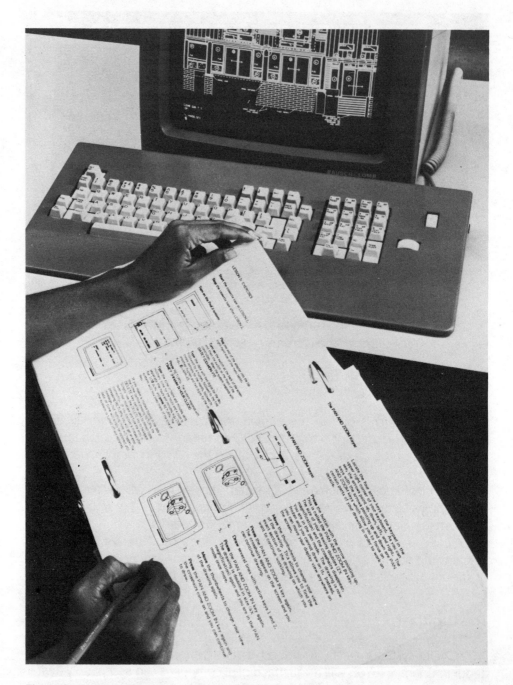

Figure 3–6 Typical keyboard *(Courtesy Bausch & Lomb)*

Figure 3–7 Digitizers *(Courtesy Bausch & Lomb)*

device for converting graphic data (drawings) into digital form before it can be entered into a CADD system's processor for storage or processing. This special device is known as the digitizer, and it may range in size from a tablet to a table (Figure 3–7).

A digitizer is an electronic drafting table that is able to convert graphic data into binary form by assigning the points which represent the end points of lines X and Y coordinates. To convert a given line into digital form, tape the drawing to the digitizer. Using the puck which is attached to the digitizer with a coiled cord, align the target site with one end point and press the ACTIVATE button. The computer will immediately compute and assign X and Y coordinates to the point. Move the puck to the other end point and activate the button. The computer calculates the distance between the points and again assigns X and Y coordinates. In this way, even the most complex drawings can be reduced to a long list of X and Y coordinates.

Cursor Control Devices

The primary interaction device in a CADD system is a small crosshair symbol—the cursor—which appears on the graphics display when the system is on. The cursor is used in many ways, such as locating and identifying data. For example, you cannot just tell the system to draw and circle; you must also tell it where. The cursor is what you use to show the computer where you would like the center of the circle to be located. Likewise, you cannot just tell the computer to erase a line; you must tell it which line to erase. Again, you use the cursor.

There are a number of different devices that can be used for controlling and manipulating the cursor. You have already seen **thumbwheels** in Figure

Figure 3–8 A puck and a digitizer *(Courtesy Bausch & Lomb)*

Figure 3–9 A light pen and a tablet *(Courtesy Bausch & Lomb)*

3–6. The horizontal thumbwheel allows the cursor to be moved from left to right on the graphics display. The vertical thumbwheel allows the cursor to be moved up and down on the graphics display. By using the two together, the cursor may be moved in any direction in steps or increments.

Another device that is used a great deal in modern CADD systems is the **puck**. It is a small, hand-held device with from one to thirteen buttons. By moving the puck over a digitizer or a graphics tablet, users can control and manipulate the cursor (Figure 3–8).

Yet another cursor control device that is often used for cursor control is the **light pen**. A light pen is used in conjunction with a graphics tablet for controlling the cursor as well as activating commands on tablet-mounted menus (Figure 3–9).

The **graphics tablet** is a small version of the digitizer in terms of its electromechanical makeup. It is used in conjunction with a light pen or puck for controlling the cursor and as a mounting device for tablet menus. Moving a puck or light pen across the surface of the graphics tablet will cause a corresponding move of the cursor on the display screen. The user in Figure 3–9 is using a light pen with a graphics tablet to activate a menu command.

Plotters

You learned that digitizers convert graphic data into digital data so that it can be entered in computer-useable form. Plotters and other output devices such as printers and hardcopy units perform exactly the opposite task. These devices take digital data from the computer and convert it to human-useable form.

There are three types of plotters used with CADD systems: pen plotters, electrostatic plotters, and photoplotters.

Pen plotters are the most easily understood because they do exactly what the drafter used to do: make drawings. Pen plotters take X and Y coordinates from the computer and use them to plot lines and alphanumeric data. In other words, they convert binary data into drawings.

Electrostatic plotters are much faster than pen plotters, although the quality of the output is considerably less. This, however, is changing as electrostatic technology continues to improve. At the present, electrostatic plotters require special paper that is not dimensionally stable. Drawings plotted electrostatically consist of images made of small dots arranged in a matrix, much like early versions of photostatic copies. At this time, some CADD systems include an electrostatic plotter as an auxiliary unit or hardcopy unit for making quick preliminary or intermediate plots prior to running pen plots. The copies can be used for checking drawings or for hard file copies. Electrostatic plotters are extremely fast. Because of this, and because they can double as printers, their use will continue to increase as the quality of electrostatic plots continues to improve.

Photoplotters are the least-used type of plotter. Photoplotters come in a variety of sizes and configurations, from small single-pen plotters to large multi-pen plotters, seen in Figures 3–10 through 3–14. They are used only in those situations which require maximum accuracy, such as printed circuit board and integrated circuit design and drafting. They operate like a pen plotter, except that the pen is replaced with a beam of light that exposes lines on special photosensitive paper.

Printers are also used in some CADD hardware configurations. Printers are either impact printers (same concept as the typewriter) or matrix printers, which make alphanumeric characters by forming tiny dots in a matrix. The printer in Figure 3–15 is a dot matrix printer. Matrix printers are fast but produce an image of lesser quality. Impact printers produce a high-quality image but are relatively slow by comparison.

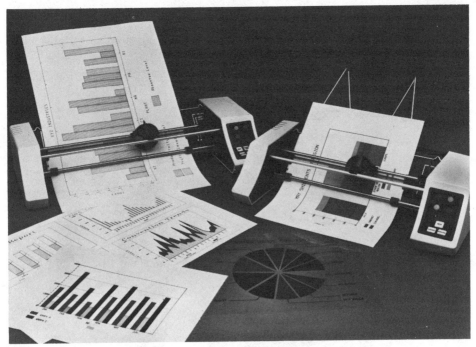

Figure 3–10 Small single-pen plotters *(Courtesy Bausch & Lomb)*

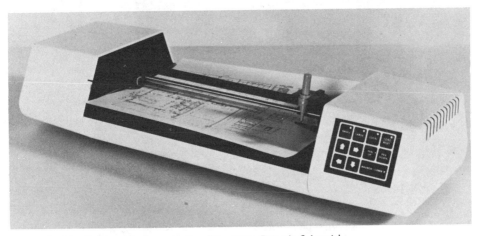

Figure 3–11 Single-pen drum plotter *(Courtesy Bausch & Lomb)*

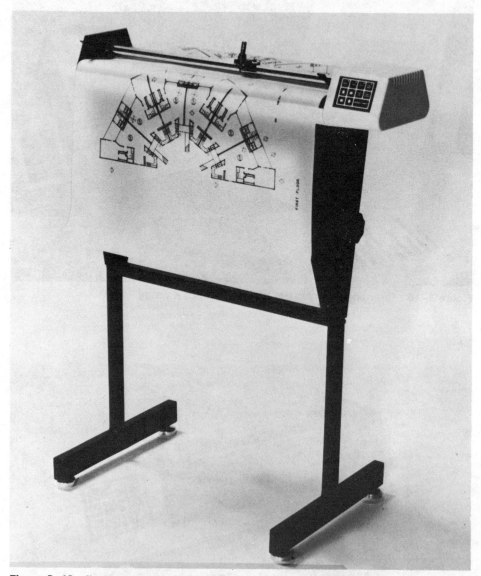

Figure 3–12 Single-pen drum plotter *(Courtesy Bausch & Lomb)*

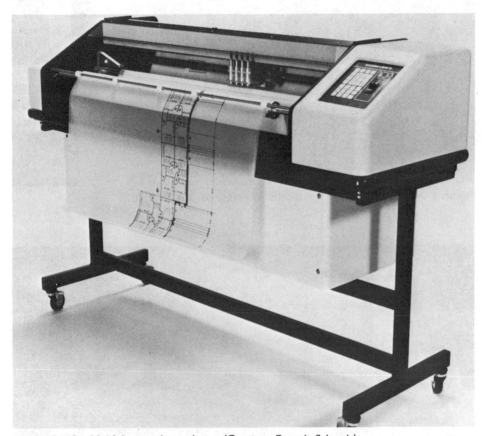

Figure 3–13   Multiple-pen drum plotter *(Courtesy Bausch & Lomb)*

Figure 3–14   Closeup of a 7-pen plotter *(Courtesy Bausch & Lomb)*

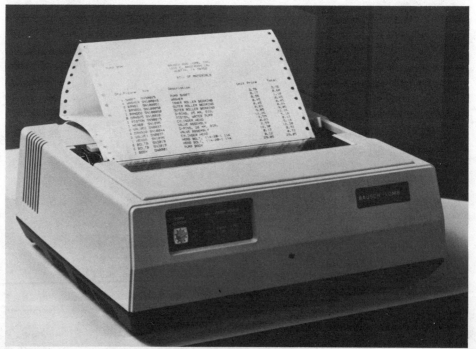

Figure 3–15   Dot matrix printer *(Courtesy Bausch & Lomb)*

CADD SOFTWARE

CADD software is a general term used to describe all of the various computer programs and different types of documentation that come with a CADD system. When most people use the term, they are referring to programs. However, the knowledgeable person in CADD should understand that CADD software includes programs, technical manuals, training manuals, program listings, menus and symbol libraries, and any audio-visual materials that may come with a CADD system purchase.

Programs

The two main types of programs that come with a CADD system purchase are operational programs and applications programs. Operational programs are the general-purpose programs that allow a CADD system to perform the general operational tasks such as allocating memory, scheduling the processor, arranging priorities of operations, interrupting operations, storing data, retrieving data from storage, and operating peripherals.

Applications programs are those designed specifically for drafting and design applications. The most commonly used applications software packages cover all of the tasks that must be performed in application areas such as mechanical design, drafting, and manufacturing; printed circuit board design, drafting, and manufacture; integrated circuit design, drafting, and manufacture; architectural design and drafting; civil engineering and drafting; mapping; technical publications; and education/training.

Technical Manuals, Training Manuals, and Program Listings

Technical manuals describe the setup, maintenance, and upkeep of the hardware. These manuals are like the owner's manuals that come with new cars, televisions, and home computers. In other words, they contain a wealth of information that you won't understand at all unless you are already an expert.

Training manuals are usually self-paced, self-teaching manuals dealing with the "how-to" aspects of CADD system operation. These can be extremely valuable for helping trained personnel train new employees or current employees who did not participate in vendor-provided training. They can also be valuable references for trained employees. Consequently, training manuals should be part of any software package that comes with a CADD purchase.

Program listings are printouts of the actual logic and code for CADD computer programs. They can be valuable references when trying to work out "bugs" that are found during setup or that occur later after the system has been in operation for a while. For a computer programming expert, a program listing is like a blueprint to a drafter or designer.

Menus and Symbols Libraries

Menus are the same thing in CADD that they are in a restaurant: a list of options. Hence, the name. In CADD, a menu or a series of menus will contain a list or visual representation of all the commands and functions available on the CADD system in question.

The designer and drafter use menus to tell the CADD system what they want it to do (e.g., draw a line, circle, ellipse, rectangle, etc.). By examining a system's menus, a designer and drafter can quickly determine all of the various commands and functions available on the system.

Menus come in several different options. The most frequently used are tablet-mounted options, screen-displayed options, and push-button options.

Tablet-mounted options are paper or plastic overlays that can be permanently or temporarily attached to graphics tablets. Commands or options on tablet-mounted menus are activated using a puck or light pen.

Screen-displayed menus are displayed on either the graphics terminal or the text terminal. Menu options on display screens are activated by touching them with a light pen or typing their letter or number on the keyboard.

Push-button menus are special menus that are matched to keys on a keyboard or a special button console. Options are activated by simply pressing the appropriate buttons.

Symbols libraries are files of special graphic symbols intrinsic to a particular drafting application (e.g., logic symbols for electronics drafting). They may be entered into the system by disk or tape. Once loaded, they can be called up and used without having to be created from scratch each time. For example, if door and window symbols were included in the symbols library of a particular CADD system's software package, the library could be loaded into the system and the user could call up the symbols as needed, rather than going through the time-consuming process of drawing them each time.

Chapter 4 contains examples of actual menus for modern CADD systems.

CADD SYSTEM USERS

The people who use CADD systems have many different titles: drafter, designer, engineer, architect, drafting manager. However, in terms of a CADD-related designation, there are two broad categories of users: CADD operators and CADD technicians.

CADD operators are people who understand the rudiments of operating a given CADD system but are not experts in design or drafting. Such people can be used for performing simple CADD tasks under the close supervision of a more qualified person. They may also be such people as sales representatives who market a given CADD system. These people may know how to operate the system they represent but may not know a great deal about the design and drafting areas they market to.

CADD technicians are skilled, knowledgeable designers or drafters in a given application who have become expert at operating a given CADD system and can use it to supplant the traditional manual procedures in their area of expertise.

The term "CADD system" is used a great deal. In fact, it has become a part of the language of design, drafting, engineering, and architecture. Although most people point at a hardware configuration and call it a CADD system, it is important to understand that, in reality, a CADD system consists of the hardware, software, and users. Each of these components must be present in order to have a real CADD system.

While it is acceptable to refer to a hardware configuration as a system as a matter of convenience or convention, one should not forget that the hardware represents only one of three critical components in a system. With this understanding, you now have the background necessary to begin a study of how design and drafting are actually accomplished on a CADD system. This is the subject of Chapter 4.

Chapter 4
DRAFTING AND DESIGN
ON A CADD SYSTEM

There are many different types of CADD systems on the market. The actual procedures used in operating these systems vary as much as the systems themselves. This is why each has its own operator's manual. However, the devices and procedures used in CADD are enough alike that they can be generalized for discussion and examination.

This chapter will present a generic explanation of how typical design and drafting tasks are performed in a CADD system and will answer the following questions:

1. What are the interaction devices used in operating CADD systems?
2. How do you log-on to a CADD system?
3. How do you create drawings on a CADD system?
4. How do you do lettering on a CADD system?
5. How do you accomplish size specification on a CADD system?
6. How do you manipulate graphic data you are working on?
7. How do you facilitate data you are working on?
8. How do you erase and perform other modifications?
9. How do you output data when you are through with it?

Before getting into the actual types of devices and processes used in performing CADD operations, you will need to develop a general understanding of the conceptual framework within which CADD operations are performed. In my workshops and seminars on CADD, I use an activity to help manual designers and drafters break out of their traditional mode of thinking toward drafting and design. This is a necessary preliminary step that will help you understand CADD much easier.

The easiest way to understand how to draft and design on a CADD system is to think of the system as a person—a drafter or designer. And one who is not very bright for that matter. Your job is to create the documentation for a simple design project. You are going to give the directions and your employee—let's just call the employee CADD SYSTEM—is going to do the work. Remember that CADD SYSTEM is not very bright. It must be told exactly what to do, when to do it, and where to do it. As to how, it can only do what it has been programmed to do.

Think about the instructions you will have to give CADD SYSTEM to get it to draw something as simple as a square with 2-inch sides. If you just say, "Draw a 2-inch square," CADD SYSTEM will be unable to respond. It will require answers to such questions as:

1. What type of line (solid, hidden, dashed, construction, etc.)?
2. What scale (full size, half size, quarter size, etc.)?
3. Where should it be drawn on the sheet?

If you try this exercise with a colleague, it will help you break out of the manual drafting way of thinking and come to understand how to operate a CADD system. It's like the game "Simon Says" with an added dimension. Not only can a CADD SYSTEM not move until told to do so, it is also limited to accepting those commands it has been programmed to carry out. After you have tried the activity explained above, you are ready to begin your study of how CADD systems are operated in generic terms.

INTERACTION DEVICES AND PROCESSES

Although voice activation may be in the making, at this time you cannot just talk to a CADD system and tell it what you what done. There are many special interaction devices that allow you to communicate with the CADD system; both hard and soft devices are used. Hard devices include light pens, pucks, joysticks, thumbwheels, keyboards, graphics tablets, and digitizers. Soft devices include the cursor that appears on the graphics display and function menus. Let's begin with the soft devices.

Soft Devices

The screen cursor is a small crosshair device which appears on the graphics display when the system is on. It is a multipurpose device that is valuable to the user. It can be used for locating data on the display, identifying data that are to be manipulated, identifying data that are to be modified, and selecting options from screen menus.

Function menus serve two purposes: (1) they show users what commands are available to them (in other words, what the system knows how to do) and (2) they give users an easy way of telling the system what functions to perform. There are several types of functions menus with different models of CADD systems. The most common types are tablet menus, screen menus, and push-button menus.

Tablet menus are plastic or paper overlays that may be permanently or temporarily attached to a graphics tablet. Each position on the menu corresponds with a position on the tablet which, in turn, corresponds with a memory location in the processor. A location or an option on a tablet menu is activated using a puck or a light pen.

Figure 4–1 is an example of a tablet menu that contains options in five general groupings: TEXT, AUTOMATIC DIMENSIONING, EDITING, FIGURE LIBRARY, and FIGURE SCALING and ROTATION. Examine Figure 4–1 closely to determine the options a user has available when this menu is mounted on a tablet. Under the TEXT heading, users may select options that specify the height of letters, several different lettering fonts (styles), horizontal and vertical spacing, and vertical or inclined lettering.

Figure 4–2 is a menu for creating and manipulating graphic data. Look closely under the CROSSHATCHING column and you will see that a user has eight different crosshatching options. Under the SPECIAL FEATURES column, a user can deal with any type or size of fillet.

Figure 4–3 is a facsimile of a screen menu for creating simple geometric characters. As you can see, a given CADD system can and usually will have several different menus and submenus. The commands in Figure 4–3 would be activated using a light pen. The user would simply touch the screen with the pen to activate the desired command. Another way of activating options on screen menus is to type the letter or number of the option when letters or numbers precede options.

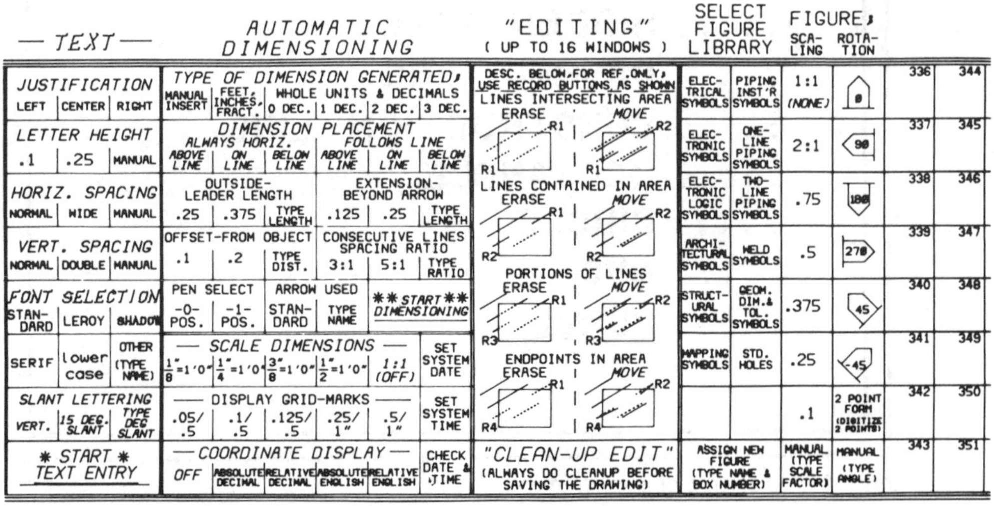

Figure 4–1   Tablet menu *(Courtesy Auto-Trol Technology Corporation)*

LAYERING			PEN SELECT	ROUNDOFF		BROKEN LINES	LINE WIDTH	DOUBLE LINES		DISPLAY CONTROL	SPECIAL FEATURES		MIRROR	CROSS-FEAT. HATCHING	3-D OPERATIONS		
WORK LAYER	DISP LAYER	EDIT LAYER		DIGI-TIZER	CRT												
LAYER 1	LAYER 1	LAYER 1	PEN 0	_NONE_	_NONE_	[⎯ ⎯] .2 −.1	WIDTH OFF	HALF-WIDTH .025	.05	DISPLAY * ALL *	_BACKSPACE_ (LAST ITEM)		MIRROR ABOUT ORIGIN		90 DEGREE ROTATION		
LAYER 2	LAYER 2	LAYER 2	PEN 1	.05	.05	[⎯ ⎯] .12−.06	WIDTH ON	.1	.15	_REFRESH DISPLAY_	*RECTANGLE* (IND.2 DIAG. PT.S FOR EACH)		ABOUT −X− AXIS		RESTORE RESTORE RESTORE		
LAYER 3	LAYER 3	LAYER 3	PEN 2	.0625	.0625	[⎯ ⎯] .1−.05	WIDTH .05	.25	MANUAL (TYPE HALF-WIDTH)	ZOOM-IN (INDICATE 2 DIAG.CORNERS)	_auto-record_		ABOUT −Y− AXIS		MANUAL ROTATION (TYPE IN ANGLE DESIRED)		
LAYER 4	LAYER 4	LAYER 4	PEN 3	.1	.1	[⎯ ⎯] .1−.1	WIDTH .1			DISPLAY AT ACT. SIZE (IND.CENTER)	SMOOTH LINE		ABOUT A DIAG. LINE (INDICATE 2 POINTS)		ISO-METRIC VIEW	DI-METRIC VIEW	TRI-METRIC VIEW
LAYER 5	LAYER 5	LAYER 5	PEN 4	.125	.125	[- - -] .05−.1	MANUAL WIDTH (TYPE WIDTH)			MOVE WINDOW (IND.CENTER)	"FILLET" 1/16 R	.1 R	ABOUT A HORIZ. LINE (INDICATE 1 POINT)		RESTORE RESTORE RESTORE		
LAYER 6	LAYER 6	LAYER 6	PEN 5	.2	.2	℄ CENTER-LINE	DISPLAY MODE *SINGLE*			_RAPID ACCESS_ IND. WINDOW	1/8 R	.2 R	ABOUT A VERT. LINE (INDICATE 1 POINT)		_perspective_ (TYPE IN DISTANCE)		
ALL LAYERS	ALL LAYERS	ALL LAYERS	PEN 6	.25	.25	PHANTOM	DISPLAY DOUBLE NORMAL OPEN			DISPLAY SORTED WINDOW (TYPE WINDOW NUMBER)	1/4 R	3/8 R	ABOUT ANY POINT		*AUTOMATIC ARROWS* START END BOTH		
MANUAL TYPE LAYER NUMBERS	MANUAL TYPE LAYER NUMBERS	MANUAL TYPE LAYER NUMBERS	PEN 7	MANUAL (TYPE DIST.)	MANUAL (TYPE DIST.)	MANUAL TYPE LENGTHS	DISPLAY DOUBLE NORMAL CLOSED			*CLEAR* WORKSPACE AREA	1/2 R	MANUAL (TYPE RADIUS)					

Figure 4–2   Tablet menu *(Courtesy Auto-Trol Technology Corporation)*

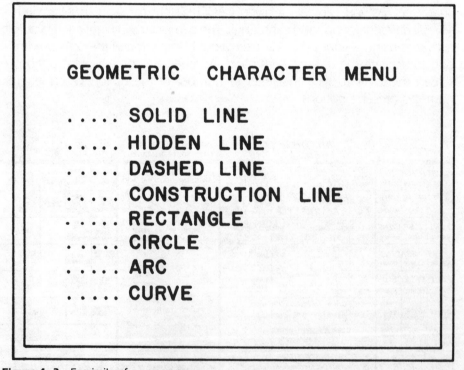

Figure 4–3   Facsimile of a screen menu

Push-button menus work one of two ways: (1) an overlay is fitted to a set of auxiliary keys on the system's keyboard and commands are activated by pressing the appropriate keys; or (2) a special push-button console comes with the system that is dedicated to menu use.

Hard Devices

There are several devices and procedures used in manipulating the screen cursor, activating menu commands, and interacting with the CADD system in general. The most commonly used devices are the light pen, puck, tablet, and keyboard. Other devices used include joysticks, thumbwheels, and trackballs.

Light pens are normally used in conjunction with a graphics tablet, such as the one in Figure 4–4. However, in some systems the light pen can be used for direct screen interaction. Joysticks are used less frequently but may still be found on several modern CADD systems. By manipulating the joystick, users manipulate the cursor. The CADD system in Figure 4–5 has a joystick immediately to the right of the numeric pad on its keyboard.

Figure 4–4 User with a light pen *(Courtesy T&W Systems Inc.)*

Figure 4–5 System with a joystick *(Courtesy MCAUTO)*

Thumbwheels are used on some systems to manipulate the cursor. Systems so configured generally have a vertical and a horizontal thumbwheel so the cursor can be moved in incremental steps to any location on the graphics display. The system in Figure 4–6 has thumbwheels immediately to the right of the numeric pad on its keyboard.

Pucks are one of the most frequently used interaction devices. They are used in conjunction with a tablet and come in models that have from one to thirteen buttons. Each button has an interactive function. The function of the button on a single-button puck is to activate the command once the puck is aligned. Multiple-button pucks have additional capabilities such as "snap-to" and "step." The system in Figure 4–7 uses a single-button puck and a graphics tablet.

Keyboards are present on all CADD systems and serve several different purposes. They can be used for entering commands by typing the name or code for the command, for activating screen menus options, for entering text on drawings, and for selecting numerous other functions, depending on the configuration of the system. Examine the different keyboards used with the CADD systems in Figure 4–4 through 4–7.

Figure 4–6   Systems with thumbwheels *(Courtesy Bausch & Lomb)*

A graphics tablet is a flat electromechanical device used in conjunction with a light pen or puck for (1) manipulating the screen cursor, (2) activating menu commands, and (3) digitizing graphic data. A graphics tablet and a digitizer are electromechanically the same in terms of basic capabilities and uses. Digitizers are usually larger and have a higher resolution rating. The graphics tablet in Figure 4–8 contains a special menu for electronics drafting. Commands are activated using a single-button puck.

Figure 4–9 is a digitizer with a multiple-button puck. Notice that it is larger than the graphics tablet in Figure 4–9. As you learned earlier, digitizers come in a variety of sizes. The puck used with a digitizer is usually a multiple-button model, since digitizers are used for inputting complex drawings, thereby requiring the user to have more capabilities than single-button models allow. Single-button models work well with graphics tablets and menus because they do nothing more than activate options large enough to be easily touched without fear of missing a close corner or detail on more complicated drawings.

Figure 4–7 System with a tablet and puck *(Courtesy Bausch & Lomb)*

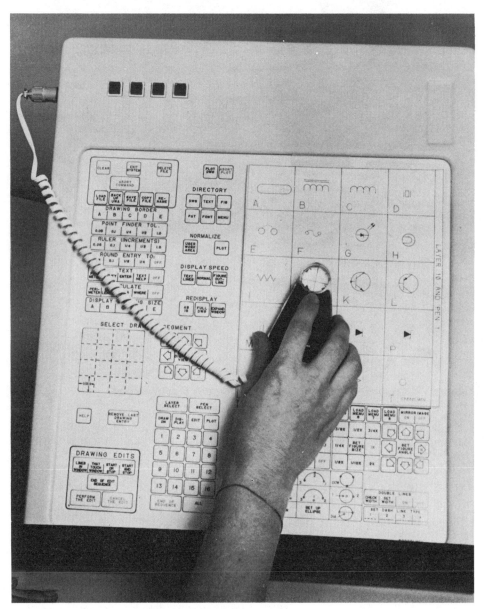

Figure 4–8 Graphics tablet *(Courtesy Bausch & Lomb)*

Figure 4–9 Digitizer with multiple pen puck *(Courtesy Bausch & Lomb)*

Now that you know the various devices and procedures used for interacting with the CADD system, you are ready to begin a study of the ways in which design and drafting tasks are accomplished on a CADD system. The first step is learning how to log-on to the system.

LOGGING-ON TO THE SYSTEM

All CADD systems have a series of steps called the **log-on sequence** that must be accomplished to gain access to the system. The log-on sequence for every system is different. However, for the purpose of illustration, the following generic sequence is provided:

Step 1
Turn on the processor and all peripherals. The normal sequence is processor first and then the peripherals in any order. However, since the order is important on some sytems, always check the operator's manual before turning on the power.

Step 2
Insert disks, diskettes, or tape into the drive unit.

Step 3
Once the software is activated, the log-on sequence is completed by responding to screen prompts such as:

    NAME?
    DATE?
    TIME?
    FILE NAME?

To respond to the NAME prompt, type your name and activate it using whatever key on the keyboard is the designated activation key (usually the RETURN or ENTER key). This will move you to the next prompt in the sequence. It is handled accordingly, and you move to the next prompt until all in the sequence have been satisfied. Once all prompts have been responded to, access to the system is gained.

GRAPHICS CREATION

Graphic data consist of points, lines, and planes. Graphic data are, of course, an integral part of most types of documentation in CADD. Figure 4–10 is an example of a drawing produced on a CADD system. This drawing is an orthographic drawing with sections of a piston casting. Take away the text (lettering, notes, dimensions, and other annotation) and you have a compilation of points, lines, and planes—remembering from basic drafting that geometric characters like circles, arcs, and curves are made of straight lines. Figures 4–11 and 4–12 are examples of three-dimensional drawings (isometric) produced on a CADD system. Again, take away the text, and all that remains is a compilation of points, lines, and planes. Therefore, in order to produce graphic data on a CADD system, one must be able to interact with the system to cause it to produce points, lines, and planes.

To assist users in creating graphic data on a CADD system, the most common forms of graphic data are programmed into the system and placed on a menu for easy access. Graphic creation commands typically found on the menus of CADD systems include:

Point	Arc
Solid line	Irregular curve
Hidden line	Polygon
Constuction line	Crosshatching
Dashed line	(various options)
Rectangle	Irregular surfaces
Circle	Meshes
Ellipse	Intersecting surfaces

For the purpose of illustration, three examples from this list can be taken and explained in generic terms. What follows are illustrated explanations of how lines, circles, and rectangles are created on a CADD system. Of course, these are generic explanations. The actual procedures will vary from system to system.

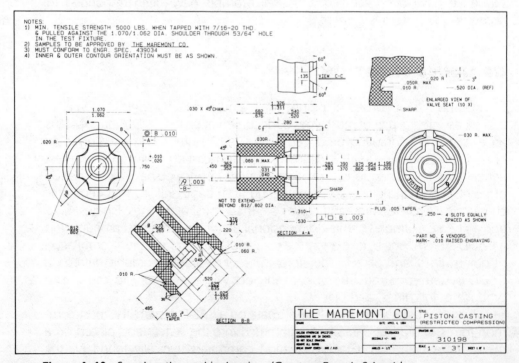

Figure 4–10 Sample orthographic drawing. *(Courtesy Bausch & Lomb)*

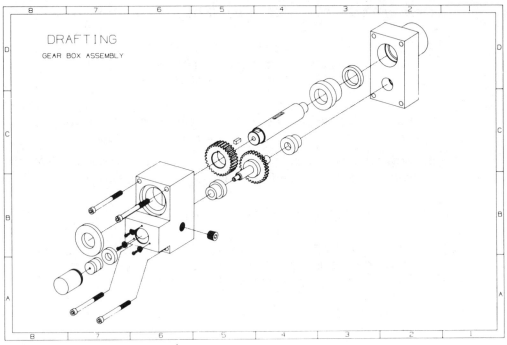

Figure 4–11   Sample isometric drawing *(Courtesy MCAUTO)*

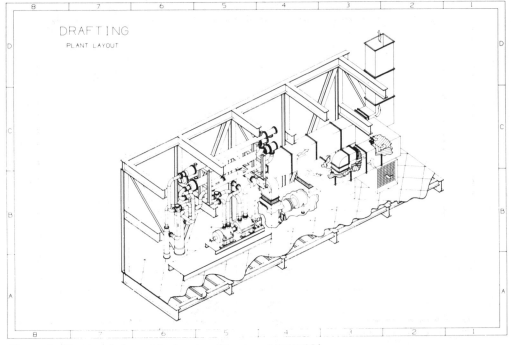

Figure 4–12   Sample isometric drawing *(Courtesy MCAUTO)*

Creating a Line on a CADD System. (Figure 4–13)

1. Activate the LINE command on the function menu. A prompt will appear on the text or graphics display:
   MARK BEGINNING POINT

2. Move the screen cursor to the desired beginning point of the line and activate the point. A prompt will appear on the graphics display:
   MARK END POINT

3. Move the screen cursor to the end point of the line and activate the point. A line will immediately form between the two points.

Creating a Rectangle on a CADD System. (Figure 4–14)

1. Activate the rectangle command on the function menu. A prompt will appear on the graphics display:
   MARK ONE CORNER

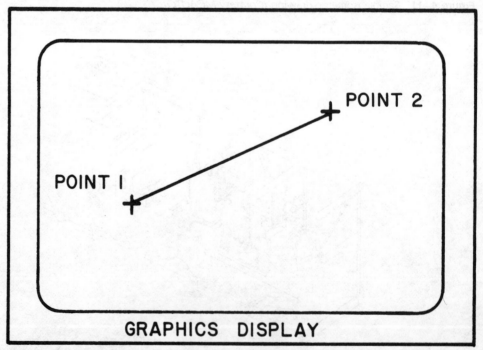

Figure 4–13 Creating a line

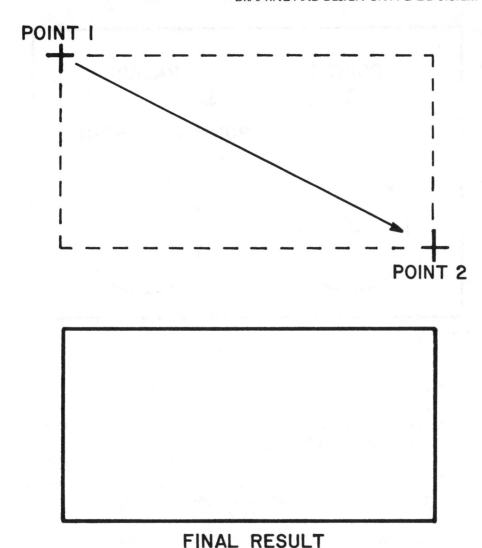

Figure 4–14   Creating a rectangle

2. Move the screen cursor to any corner—say, the upper left-hand corner—of the rectangle, and activate the point. A prompt will appear on the graphics display:

MARK THE DIAGONAL CORNER

3. Move the screen cursor to the diagonal corner and activate the point. A rectangle will immediately appear on the graphics display.

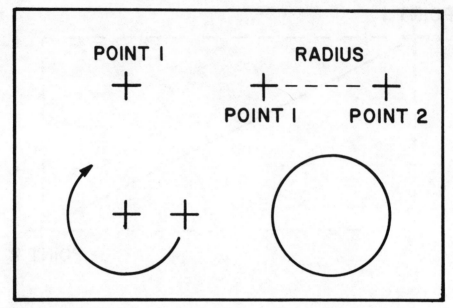

Figure 4–15 Creating a circle

Creating a Circle on a CADD System. (Figure 4–15)

1. Activate the CIRCLE command on the function menu. A prompt will appear on the graphics display:
   MARK CIRCLE'S CENTER

2. Move the screen cursor to the centerpoint of the circle and activate the point. A prompt will appear on the graphics display:
   MARK RADIUS

3. Move the screen cursor away from the centerpoint a distance equal to the circle's radius and activate the point. A circle will immediately form around the centerpoint.

TEXT CREATION

Most types of documentation in design and drafting include text. **Text** is the general term used for any type of alphanumeric data used on any type of documentation. Notes, legends, dimensions, descriptions, specifications, schedule entries, and any other type of what in manual drafting is referred to as lettering is considering text in CADD.

Text is entered by activating the TEXT command on a menu and typing in the desired text. An exception to this is the automatic dimensioning function which, on some systems, will automatically enter dimension.

Text created on a CADD system is clear, legible, and pleasing to the eye— one of the advantages of CADD over manual drafting.

SIZE SPECIFICATION

Size specifiers are commands that allow users to indicate the actual size of graphic data that has been produced. The generic names for commands typically found in this category are **automatic dimension** and **dimension**.

Automatic dimension is a function that takes advantage of a characteristic that is intrinsic to computers. Digital computers plot graphic data on the graphics screen based on X and Y coordinates. Since this is the case, a computer must calculate the distance between coordinates in order to plot a line. This means that once the computer has plotted a line on the graphic display, it already knows what its dimension is. This characteristic enables CADD systems to have an automatic dimensioning capability.

Most systems also have normal dimensioning capabilities for those occasions when automatic dimensioning may not be wanted, such as when a part is not to be dimensioned completely.

The following explanation outlines the generic procedures used in automatically dimensioning a line on a CADD system.

Automatic Dimensioning on a CADD System. (Figure 4–16)

1. Activate the AUTOMATIC DIMENSION command on the function menu. A prompt will appear on the graphics or text display:
   MARK DIMENSION BEGINNING

2. Move the screen cursor to the beginning of the line that is to be dimensioned and activate the point. A prompt will appear on the display:
   MARK DIMENSION END POINT

3. Move the screen cursor to the end of the line that is to be dimensioned and activate the point. A prompt will appear on the display:
   MARK DISTANCE FROM OBJECT

4. Move the screen cursor to indicate how far away from the object the dimension line is to be and activate the point. Extension lines, dimension lines, arrowheads, and the dimension will immediately appear on the display.

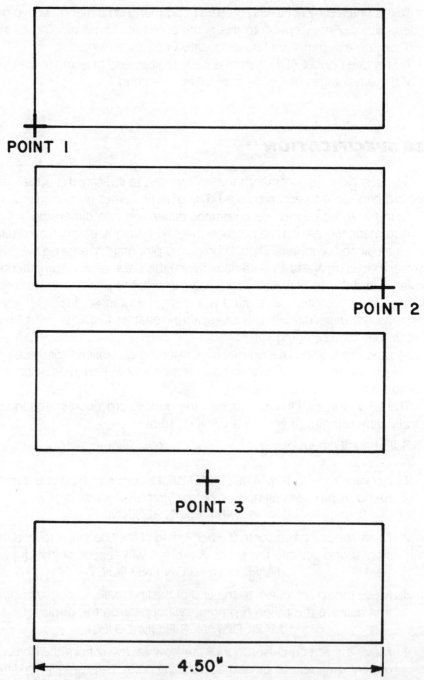

Figure 4-16 Dimensioning

MODIFYING DATA

One of the most frequently used manual tools is the eraser. CADD system users must also have a means for modifying data on which they are working. Not only do they have *a* means, they have several. In fact, data modification is one of the strong points of a CADD system. Typical modification functions available to CADD systems users include:

Edit
Erase
Delete
Redraw
Scale

Edit is a command that comes from word processing and is used in the same way on a CADD system. It allows users to insert, correct, rearrange, and revise text.

Erase is a command used to eliminate all data displayed on the screen without eliminating the file. It is the CADD system user's equivalent of starting over with a new sheet of paper.

Delete allows users to eliminate specific items of data such as an alphanumeric character or a line. Many systems have a subfunction called **box delete** in which the user creates a box around an area or a group of data and everything in the box is deleted.

Redraw is a command that allows users to clean up the display by getting rid of accumulated "garbage." Garbage is partial data left over that was not completely deleted. In the creation of a complex drawing, garbage will frequently collect on the display. By activating the redraw command, CADD system users can easily get rid of the garbage. When the redraw command is given, the entire display will go blank. Then the image will be "repainted" but without the garbage.

Scale is a command used for increasing or decreasing the size of an image on the display. For example, if you have created a 2-inch square on the display at full size, you could reduce it to half-size, quarter-size, etc., by using the scale command. You could also increase its size by using the scale command and specifying 2×, 3×, 4×, etc.

The scale command should not be confused with the zoom-in command, which is a data manipulation function explained in the next section.

MANIPULATING DATA

Something that can be done on a CADD system which really has no manual equivalent is easy manipulation of data. Manipulation commands coupled with modification commands make corrections and revisions effortless on a CADD system. In manual drafting, they represent one of the least-productive, most cost-ineffective tasks that must be performed.

The generic names for manipulation commands typically found in a CADD system include:

Move
Copy
Mirror
Zoom-in
Pan

The **move** command allows users to move data from one location on the display to another without having to redraw it. This concept is illustrated in Figure 4–17. In this example, the user incorrectly placed the right-side view of a part on the left side of the part. This violates the rules of orthographic projection. To correct the problem, the user can take advantage of the move function.

1. Activate the MOVE command on the function menu. A prompt will appear on the display:
   IDENTIFY MOVE FROM POINT

2. Move the screen cursor to a functional point on the data to be moved (centerpoint, corner, endpoint, etc.) and activate the point. A prompt will appear on the display:
   IDENTIFY MOVE TO POINT

3. Move the screen cursor to the point on the display that represents the desired position of the functional point you have chosen and activate the point. The data to be moved will go blank in its old position and will reappear in the new position.

The **copy** command is a time-saving function intrinsic to CADD. It allows users to create data once and then copy it as many times as needed without having to recreate it each time. An example of how this function might be used is with windows on a house elevation. Many houses use the same type and size of window repeatedly. When this is the case, the user need only create the

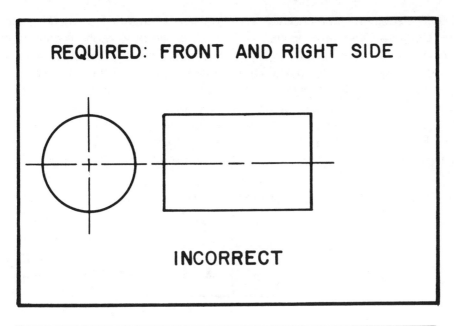

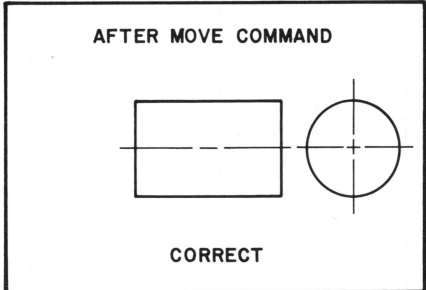

Figure 4–17 MOVE function

window once. Each time the same window is needed, it can be copied using the copy command. The copy command works just like the move command, except that the original does not disappear after it is copied.

The **zoom-in** command is a handy function for making extremely detailed and crowded work easier to deal with. By activating the zoom-in command, users can cause graphic data to *appear* to increase in size, similar to the effect gained when you blow up or enlarge a photograph. You should understand that what is actually happening each time the zoom-in command is given is that your eyes are being brought closer to the object, thus the appearance of the enlargement. You do not change the scale of the data by zooming-in on it.

Figure 4–18 is an example of what happens when the zoom-in command is given. A square has been created on the graphics display and quartered. Each

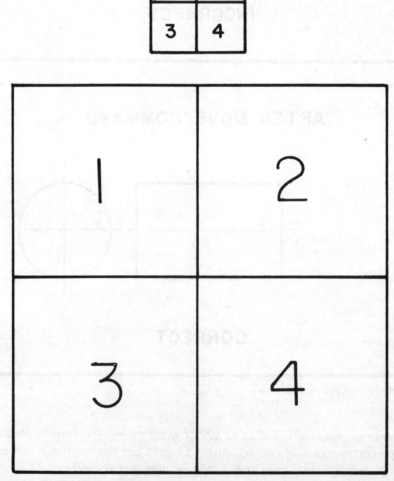

Figure 4–18 ZOOM-IN function

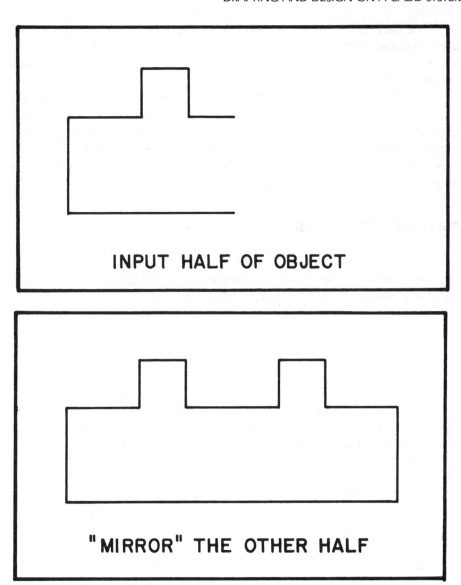

Figure 4–19 MIRROR function

quarter of the square is numbered. The actual size of the square is represented by the top figure. The bottom figure represents how the square would appear on the display after the zoom-in command has been given. Each time the command is repeated, the object appears to increase in size proportionately. Understand that if you decide to give the plot command while an object is zoomed-in on, it will plot the actual size or the size it appeared prior to the zoom-in command.

The **pan** command is the opposite of the zoom-in command. It allows users to get a distant view of data for a wider or overall perspective. Activating the pan command is like walking farther away from an object to gain a broader perspective.

The **mirror** command is another time-saving command that can be used when creating symmetrical objects on the graphics display. When an object is symmetrical, the mirror command allows users to create only half of it and mirror the other half. Once half of a symmetrical object has been produced, a user need only activate the mirror command on the function menu and the other half will immediately appear, as shown in Figure 4–19.

FACILITATING DATA

There are a number of functions needed for general system operation and data management. These functions are known as **facilitation functions.** Typical facilitation functions found in most CADD systems include:

Save
File
Library
Layer

Facilitation commands give users the ability to manage, control, and store data. The **save** command is used when you wish to keep data in a file and the file itself stored either in the main memory or on a secondary storage device. The save command is given on many systems prior to outputting data so the data are not eliminated in the process.

The **file** command is used for creating files under which data are collected. You might initiate a file and give it the name "JOB 2500." Under this file name, you might create and store several different items of documentation that relate to Job 2500.

Library is a command that allows users to form such time- and work-saving items as symbols libraries. Many companies have specific symbols and graphic data that are used over and over. These symbols can be created once, placed in a library, stored under the library designation, and called up for use as needed. The library function also allows users to access libraries that came with the system as part of the software package.

Layer is a command that allows users to create and store data on different layers. An example of the use of layer function might occur in architectural drafting. In a set of house plans, the HVAC, electrical, and plumbing plans are superimposed over a simplified version of the floor plan. In manual drafting, the floor plan must be created for each separate mechanical plan. This is time consuming and not cost effective.

In CADD, the floor plan can be created once on a designated layer. Then each mechanical plan can be superimposed on another layer without requiring a new floor plan each time. The layer function also comes in handy for design review. In the same example, a designer could create the floor plan on one layer, the HVAC plan on another, and the plumbing plan on another. To review the design for overlaps or other design problems, the various layers could be assigned different colors and then superimposed on each other. Conflicts and overlaps could be easily seen and corrected. Data on one layer could be modified and manipulated without interfering with data on another layer.

OUTPUTTING DATA

When documentation has been created, checked, corrected, revised, and stored, or at any place in the process where hardcopy is needed, it can be output in human-useable form. The three output methods used with CADD systems for hardcopy are printing, plotting, and hardcopy (an electrostatic copy).

There is a series of steps to execute in preparing to output data, such as turning on the output device, loading it if necessary, and formatting if necessary. However, once the output devices have been prepared, CADD system users need only activate the appropriate command (e.g., PLOT, PRINT, COPY).

Operating a CADD system, regardless of the model or manufacturer, is a matter of activating commands that are keyed to functions and responding to prompts to give the system even more specific instructions before it attempts to perform the desired task. Most CADD systems will have many more options than the few outlined in this chapter. However, those presented herein represent the basics. And the procedures outlined for making use of these functions are representative of how most CADD systems are interacted with, at least in generic terms.

If a user understands that a system's capabilities are set forth in menus and submenus, and that menu options are activated using a variety of devices such as pucks, light pens, or key commands, and that most commands are accompanied by a series of prompts that must be responded to, he or she can quickly learn to operate any CADD system.

Chapter 5

JUSTIFYING THE CADD CONVERSION

I am often asked the question, "Is CADD cost effective?" The best answer I can give is "It can be." This is not the answer people want to hear when trying to convince management to take the plunge into CADD. Management can only be convinced to approve an investment in CADD through figures that prove it will be a wise investment. Such justifications are not usually the strong suits of technical people, nor do they represent why technical people become interested in CADD.

Technical people who read professional journals and attend conferences and conventions are drawn to CADD because it will increase their capabilities while eliminating much of the boring, nonproductive parts of thier jobs. CADD offers drafters and designers many advantages over manual drafting, including more attractive documentation, consistent documentation, and greater accuracy. However, when the time comes to convince management to take the plunge, you have to talk dollars and cents.

Trying to arrive at a bottom-line figure for management is not an easy task. This is what makes some technical people uncomfortable in trying to justify CADD. There are so many unsure variables that will impact the eventual cost effectiveness of CADD. Most people familiar with CADD have heard the horror stories of companies that attempted a CADD conversion back in the late 1960s or early 1970s, only to have to back out of the conversion and return to a manual operation. Fortunately, since that time, technology and prices have changed considerably for the better. However, the memories still linger.

My recommendation to technical people hoping to justify a CADD conversion is to lay out a justification package that spans a five-year period using the "best case" and "worst case" approach. Then outline the many variables that can affect the cost effectiveness of CADD in a negative way as well as strategies for controlling these variables to the extent that they can be controlled.

This chapter will help technical people learn to prepare a justification for a CADD conversion that will be valid for their companies. Such a justification will take time and work, but it will yield much more reliable data than the generalized justifications available from vendors and technical journals. What will be important to the managers of your company is figures computed for your company. You will have to rely to some extent on figures from other companies, but they can be modified to fit your company's situation. To help you, this chapter covers the following topics:

Determining the cost effectiveness of CADD
Other factors in justifying a CADD conversion

DETERMINING THE COST EFFECTIVENESS OF CADD

The truth is that you won't know if CADD will be cost-effective at your company until the conversion is complete and enough time has elapsed to examine the balance sheet. However, you can make an educated forecast and help facilitate its eventual success by completing several tasks:

1. Identify several companies similar to yours in size, products, and procedures and discuss the cost effectiveness of CADD with them. Make a record of the productivity improvements they have actually realized from CADD each year for a five-year period. Also make a record of hidden or unforeseen costs and variables that affected the conversion in a positive or a negative way.
2. Develop a manual versus CADD financial forecast for a five-year period.
3. Identify variables that can positively and negatively impact the cost effectiveness of the CADD conversion.
4. Develop strategies for taking advantage of positive factors and controlling (to the extent possible) the negative factors.

CONTACTING OTHER COMPANIES

Forecasting the cost effectiveness of CADD over a five-year period is like trying to plan your family budget five years in advance and then live according to the plan. The problem comes in trying to identify all the unforeseen variables and hidden costs that will inevitably show up—of course, at the worst possible time. This is why it is so important to talk to other companies that have undergone a CADD conversion. And the closer in makeup and size these companies are to yours, the better. They will have developed the wisdom that comes with experience, and you can benefit from their successes and their mistakes.

It is important to get both a feel for the general attitude of these experienced colleagues toward the CADD conversion and some specific data about the conversion. Having gone through a conversion, do they, in retrospect, feel good or bad about it and why? More specific questions that you should ask are:

1. What productivity improvements did you experience in each of the first five years after the conversion?
2. Did you hire CADD specialists to assist with the transition or rely on existing employees?
3. If you hired specialists, how many of what type for how long and at what salaries?
4. What unforeseen positive and negative factors evolved, and what did you do about them?

DEVELOPING THE FINANCIAL FORECAST

Your development of a forecast of the financial impact of CADD should proceed in six steps:

1. Develop a forecast of your company's expected workload over a five-year period (at least).
2. Forecast the personnel, facility, and materials needs brought about by the workload forecasted in step 1.
3. Forecast the overall cost that the personnel, facility, and materials from step 2 will result in.
4. Forecast the cost of a CADD conversion that would take the place of step 2.
5. Forecast the labor and cost savings that will result from CADD over the five-year period.
6. Compare the data for the manual option (steps 2 and 3) with the data for the CADD option (steps 4 and 5).

Accomplishing step 1 will require a collaborative effort of design and drafting, contracts, and sales/marketing personnel. If it is determined that the workload forecast for the upcoming five-year period is enough of an increase to require additional personnel, space, and corresponding materials, a CADD conversion is definitely indicated. If the workload is projected to remain stable or decline, a conversion to CADD is not indicated unless, of course, your company plans a corresponding reduction in its workforce.

Normally companies that are not forecasting an increased workload would not be prime candidates for a CADD conversion. But there are exceptions to this rule. One is the case of companies that have determined a conversion to CADD will help them secure additional contracts. Some campanies are beginning to find that CADD-prepared documentation is a requirement in order to bid on certain jobs. If this is the case, your company should determine what percentage of potential additional workload might be forthcoming as the result of a CADD conversion. If it is not significant, you might consider subcontracting the documentation to a CADD service bureau. CADD service bureaus are companies that prepare documentation on CADD systems on a subcontracting basis for other companies that have a need. They are strictly a service and do not normally provide the engineering and design or become involved in the manufacture or construction of the product.

Another case in which a CADD conversion might be indicated even without forecasted growth is when a decline in the workload is expected and is to be accompanied by a reduction in the work force. Some companies might decide to expand the scope of the planned reduction and implement a CADD conversion at the same time.

For illustration, assume the normal circumstance that a forecasted increase in the workload has caused your company to look for alternatives, and one being considered is CADD. You have the workload forecast in hand. The next step is to determine how the workload breaks out in terms of personnel, facilities, and materials. In this step you will need to answer four questions:

1. What types of positions will be required by the increased workload (designers, engineers, architects, drafters, secretaries, etc.)?
2. How many man-years of work are forecasted for each position identified?
3. How many new square feet of space will be required to support and accommodate the new personnel?
4. What types of tools, equipment, and other materials will be required to support the increased personnel and facility and how much?

Example 5–1 is a Forecasting Worksheet for the Manual Option. It is designed to assist in the compilation of data that can be used in making a comparison between the manual option and the CADD option.

Under "Personnel Costs," positions that might be listed, depending on the type of company, include engineer, architect, designer, checker, senior drafter, drafter, junior drafter, tracer, engineering secretary, and clerk. Under "Man-Years," the number of man-years forecasted for each position are listed. The man-years multiplied by the median income for the five-year period will

Example 5–1

Forecasting Worksheet for the Manual Option

Time Period _____

PERSONNEL COSTS

Position	Man-Years	Salary Costs	Benefits	Total

Personnel Subtotal _____

FACILITY COSTS

Type of Space	Cost per Square Foot	Total

Facility Subtotal _____

MATERIALS COSTS

Type of Material	Cost	Total

Materials Subtotal _____

Grand Total, Manual Option _____

produce the entries for the "Salary Costs" column. Under the "Benefits" column, all insurance, retirement, Social Security, and other company-specific benefit costs are listed as a total for each position. The position totals are computed, and their sum represents the personnel costs subtotal for the manual option.

In forecasting facility costs, the types of space that might be listed include office space, storage space, work space, copying and reproduction space, and conference room space. It is best to use a typical cost-per-square-foot figure for each type of space rather than an overall average for the total of all space required. This will yield a more accurate cost estimate. The sum of the totals for all of the facility entries is the subtotal of facility costs for the manual option.

The types of materials that might be listed in the "Materials Costs" forecast are all items necessary to equip and support the expanded work force. Typical entries will include furniture, reproduction equipment, storage cabinets for files and drawings, manual drafting tools, and expendable supplies. The sum of the personnel, facility, and materials costs yields a grand total projection for the manual option.

The next step involves forecasting the cost of the CADD option. This involves determining initial hardware costs, initial software costs, upgrading and expansion costs for hardware and software, training costs, maintenance costs, and facility adaptation costs. Example 5–2 is a Forecasting Worksheet for the CADD Option.

EXAMPLE 5–2

Forecasting Worksheet for the Cadd Option

Time Period _____

INITIAL HARDWARE COSTS

Item	Quantity	Unit Cost	Total
Processors			
Work stations*			
Digitizers			
Plotters			
Printers			
Hardcopy units			

Hardware Subtotal _____

INITIAL SOFTWARE COSTS

Type	Quantity	Unit Cost	Total
Operational			
Applications			
Symbols libraries			
Optional menus			
Technical manuals			

Software Subtotal _____

*Includes graphics terminal, text terminals, keyboards, graphics tablets, and cursor control devices.

UPGRADING COSTS

Area	Year 1	Year 2	Year 3	Year 4	Year 5	Total
Hardware						
Software						

Upgrading Subtotal _____

TRAINING COSTS

Type	Initial Cost	Updating Costs	Total
Management			
Beginning			
Advanced			

Training Subtotal _____

MAINTENANCE COSTS

Type	Year 1	Year 2	Year 3	Year 4	Year 5	Total
Hardware						
Software						

Maintenance Subtotal _____

FACILITY ADAPTATION COSTS

Type	Total
Electrical system adaptations	
Environmental control system adaptations	
Flooring adaptations	
Wall adaptations	
Miscellaneous adaptations	

Facility Adaptation Costs Subtotal _____

MISCELLANEOUS COSTS

Type	Total
Expendable supplies	
Specialists and consultants hired	

Miscellaneous Costs Subtotal _____
Grand Total, CADD Option _____

The entries under each major subheading are listed in detail. The sum of the subtotals for the major cost headings yields a grand total for the CADD option.

The grand totals for the manual and CADD options do not tell the whole story and should not be directly compared. Before beginning to compare data, another step should be accomplished. This step involves answering the question, "Can the projected workload be handled by CADD?"

To answer this question, you will have to project the productivity improvements over the five-year period from the CADD conversion. One source of data will be vendors, but don't stop with them. Collect figures from other companies similar in makeup to yours that have undergone a CADD conversion.

A good approach is to record the worst-case and best-case figures available. Once they have been recorded, they can be used to project annual labor savings which, in turn, can be used in forecasting actual cost savings (see Figure 5–1).

In Figure 5–1, the worst-case figures for Year One are 1:1. This means that the productivity that can be expected is the same for CADD and the manual option. This would be attributed to several factors, such as employees who were slow to accept and learn CADD. In Year Two, the productivity ratio begins to improve and favor CADD (2:1). This pattern continues through Year Five with a final productivity ratio of 5:1. In the worst case in this example, significant labor savings would accrue after a conversion to CADD.

In this figure the best-case figures for Year One are 2:1. They increase steadily to 6:1 over the projected five-year period. In the best case, significant labor savings will take place each year for the five-year period.

After the worst- and best-case productivity improvement forecasts have been made, they can be used for computing labor and cost savings. The savings for each year should be computed individually and then totalled. The number to begin with is the total man-years projected for a given year. For the purpose of illustration, take man-year two in the worst case example and assume 6 man-years were projected for the manual option.

Applying the 2:1 productivity ratio to the 6 man-years yields a CADD equivalent of 3 man-years. This is a savings of 3 man-years of labor caused by the CADD conversion in the worst case. The cost of 3 man-years can be computed, and the savings brought about by the CADD option for Year Two of the worst case example can be determined. A sample computation is shown in Example 5–3.

Using a labor cost per man-year of $30,000, the manual option for Year Two of the Worst-case example will cost $180,000. The CADD equivalent for

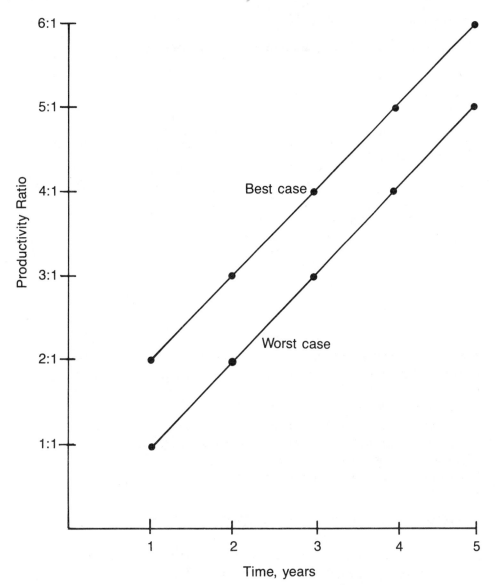

Figure 5–1 Sample comparison of best case and worst case for productivity improvement projections for a CADD system

Year Two will cost $90,000. This means the 2:1 productivity improvement realized from CADD will save $90,000 in the second year of the worst-case forecast.

Example 5-3

Sample Labor/Cost Savings Computation

Year Number _____2_____

Option	Number of Man-Years	Labor Cost * Per Man-Year, $	Cost, $
Manual	6	30,000	180,000
CADD	3 (equivalent)	30,000	90,000

Total Anticipated Cost Savings for the Year: $90,000

*Hourly rate used to arrive at the labor cost per man-year should take into account benefits and salary increases that might occur during the year in question.

The same procedure is applied to the remaining years of the worst-case example and all years of the best-case example. A total five-year savings projection for both the worst and the best cases is determined. Many companies find that the cost savings realized over a five-year period will pay the cost of the CADD conversion.

Even now the whole picture is not available. Other factors such as investment credits and tax breaks should also be investigated by your company's financial personnel. In addition, factors that can tend to help or impede success in a CADD conversion should also be identified.

VARIABLES THAT CAN AFFECT THE CONVERSION

The financial forecast developed in the preceding section contained a best case and a worst case. You should understand that even the worst-case scenario is not automatic. A number of factors can affect the transition to CADD in such a way that the conversion fails completely. The forecast in the preceding section is what *can* be gained from CADD if things go smoothly or even relatively so.

In attempting to justify a conversion to CADD, factors that can help or hurt the transition should be identified. After they have been identified, strategies can be developed for controlling—to the extent possible—the negative factors and bringing the positive to bear.

Some Negative Factors

What follows is a list of some of the variables which can have a negative impact on a CADD conversion. Some of the factors can be controlled, or at least partially controlled. Some cannot be controlled at all.

- Downturns in the economy which can invalidate forecasted increases in the company's workload over the five-year period
- Rejection of the CADD conversion by critical design and drafting personnel
- Failure of the vendor to meet shipping and installation schedules and deadlines
- A poor after-purchase relationship with the vendor
- Bankruptcy of the vendor
- Workflow interruptions due to maintenance problems with hardware and software

Some Positive Factors

It might go without saying that the opposite cases of those factors listed above can have a positive impact on the CADD conversion. This fact is worth stating so that you can attempt to ensure the opposites, as listed below, are in fact what occur rather than their negative counterparts.

- Better-than-predicted increases in the workload due to unexpected upturns in the economy
- Enthusiastic acceptance of CADD by critical design and drafting personnel
- Vendor meets or exceeds all shipping and installation schedules and deadlines
- Positive after-purchase relationship with the vendor evolves and is maintained
- Continued fiscal soundness and growth on the part of the vendor due to continually improved products and services
- Few significant workflow interruptions due to good maintenance and performance of the CADD systems

Obviously, you will have little control over unexpected upturns and downturns in the economy. However, you can have at least a degree of control over the remaining factors. Strategies for ensuring a successful CADD conversion are the subject of Chapter 6, "Implementing CADD."

Chapter 6
IMPLEMENTING CADD

By now you are beginning to be knowledgeable about CADD as a concept, the various vendors that manufacture and market CADD systems, and how to approach the justification question. Now it's time to begin thinking about implementation. This is the critical phase that will determine how CADD is accepted and if it will succeed or fail.

In order to have a smooth conversion to CADD, you will need to plan the conversion carefully. Before you can develop a CADD implementation plan, you will need answers to four questions. These questions and their answers are the subject of this chapter:

1. What is the best approach to take in implementing CADD?
2. How can potential vendors be evaluated?
3. How can the proper system be evaluated?
4. How will CADD implementation affect the company?

RECOMMENDED APPROACH TO CADD IMPLEMENTATION

What is it you purchase when the decision is made to implement CADD? Most people, in responding to this question, say "hardware and software." These, of course, are the obvious components of a CADD purchase. However, three other elements should not be overlooked: service, training, and after-purchase commitments.

There are five elements of the CADD purchase. It is possible to purchase the elements from different vendors on a lowest-bid basis and appear to save money. However, this scattered approach is not recommended, especially for people who are unfamiliar with CADD.

The recommended approach to CADD implementation is the **turnkey** approach. The turnkey approach is a package deal concept in which the hardware, software, service, training, and after-purchase commitments all come from one vendor. That vendor may not actually manufacture all of the hardware or even develop the software, but it does package and market them as a turnkey system.

Buying a CADD system is much like buying a car. If you are an experienced mechanic and have time on your hands, you might save a little on the initial capital outlay by purchasing a body from one place, an engine from another, and a drive train from yet another. However, if you are not a mechanic, you wouldn't risk this approach. The same can be said in undertaking a CADD conversion.

The turnkey approach to a CADD conversion can save companies a great many headaches, especially those that are new to CADD. In order to adopt the turnkey approach in implementing CADD, you will need to know more about the five basic components of the purchase package.

The Hardware Component

What should the vendor supply in terms of hardware, and what does the vendor not supply? Understanding the vendor/buyer relationship is important to successful implementation. The vendor should supply the processor, all peripheral equipment, accessories, and any nonstandard furniture required to set up the system.

The following generic checklist will help you develop a more specific checklist for your implementation plan:

Processor
Disk drive unit
Graphics terminal
Text terminal (if applicable)
Keyboard(s)
Cursor control devices (tablet, light pen, puck, thumbwheels, joystick, trackball)
Digitizers
Plotters (pen, electrostatic, photo)
Printers (impact, matrix)
Function menus
Interfacing cables
Miscellaneous electrical control and protection devices
Startup supplies (disks, pens, ink, vellum, paper, polyester film, magnetic tape)

There are a number of auxiliary hardware needs that must either accompany or precede a CADD hardware purchase. These are the responsibility of the buyer, not the vendor. They include:

1. Equipment to control the heat and humidity of the facility that will house the CADD system(s). The cooling and humidity requirements of a given system must be determined from potential vendors well in advance of implementation so that facility adaptations can be made if necessary.
2. Equipment for augmenting and controlling electrical power to the system(s) if normal electrical systems are not sufficient. This determination should be made well in advance of implementation. Often, normal electrical systems can provide adequate power but do not provide "surge" protection.
3. Building materials for any facility adaptations that might be required. Facility adaptations should be identified well in advance of implementation. Concrete floors may need to be modified to protect the system(s) from vibration. Old-fashioned chalkboards that may be available for use in "brainstorming" sessions should be replaced with the more modern dust-free boards.
4. Telecommunications equipment for linking and networking systems and locations.
5. Furniture beyond that included in the purchase package. This should be determined well in advance of implementation.

The Software Component

The vendor should supply a complete software package that will maximize the usefulness of the system(s) to the buyer. The following generic checklist will help you develop a more specific checklist for your implementation plan:

Operational software
Applications software
Technical manuals
Operator's manuals
Training manuals
Program listings
Log books for recording maintenance
Audio-visual training materials (optional)

The Service Component

After-purchase service is an important part of the CADD implementation package. And the less a buyer knows about CADD, the more important this component is. Service that should be provided by the vendor includes:

Hardware service and maintenance
Software service and maintenance
Management service and assistance

Hardware service involves initial installation and startup, and testing of all hardware components in the configuration. Once the system is operational, preventive maintenance, upkeep, and repair should also be available according to a schedule established in the initial guarantee and any additional maintenance agreements entered into.

Software service should include initial installation, setup, and "debugging." Once the system is operational, periodic software maintenance should also be provided according to the specifications set forth in the initial guarantee and any additional software maintenance agreements entered into.

Management assistance is a service that is a must and should not be overlooked. The type, degree, and amount of assistance provided varies from vendor to vendor. In many cases, what is provided may depend on what is asked for. Management services that should be asked for include:

Access to "user groups." These are self-help organizations, usually independent of the vendor, made up of companies that have purchased systems from the same vendor.

Advice on how to plan and manage the implementation based on experience with other installations.

Comparative data on what CADD personnel are paid in similar installations.

Advice on hiring temporary CADD experts to keep the work flowing smoothly while the regular design and drafting staff is learning CADD.

The Training Component

This may be the most important component of the entire CADD implementation package. In fact, too often too little attention is given this component. In the long run, the cost effectiveness of CADD on a long-term basis will depend on the acceptance, skills, and creativity of all personnel involved at all levels. These things begin with good, solid CADD training.

There are several different levels of personnel who will require training as part of the CADD implementation package. The obvious training need is for people who will operate the system(s). There are three categories of employees who will operate the system(s) frequently: (1) general operational employees who perform simple tasks such as digitizing and running the plotter, (2) drafters who perform most of the day-to-day documentation work as well as the checking of that work, and (3) professional personnel such as designers, engineers, and architects. Each of these groups has individual needs from the CADD system. Training for each of these groups should be geared toward meeting those needs. For example, general operators do not need to sit through training sessions on three-dimensional modelling.

Another level that should not be overlooked in arranging training is supervisory and management personnel in the area of design and drafting. Training of these individuals should begin before installation of the system(s) and continue for a stated period of time after installation. Training for supervisory and management personnel should include:

Explanations of the various types of hardware and software maintenance agreements available and the advantages and disadvantages of each.

Explanations of how users will be trained and how the learning curve can be expected to affect productivity in the short term and the long term.

Problems to expect during implementation, and suggested and proven remedies.

Assistance with developing a comprehensive implementation plan.

Warranty Obligations

Warranty obligations that are part of the CADD implementation package are of two types: formal and informal. Formal warranty obligations are those that exist in writing. These guarantees come with the system and cover hardware and software for a specified period of time, just like the guarantee that comes with a new car. They also include any additional maintenance agreements that may be entered into which extend beyond the initial guarantees.

Maintenance agreements on hardware vary with type and cost. The cost of an agreement will depend on the geographic proximity of the vendor and the buyer and on the amount of downtime a buyer feels is acceptable. Maintenance agreements on software should cover both "bugs" that occur while using the system and periodic updates and improvements to the software.

The formal, written agreements are important. But equally important are the unwritten, informal warranty obligations. In fact, many people who have gone through a CADD conversion feel the informal obligations are even more important.

Informal warranty obligations are based on the vendor's desire to maintain a positive image and a good reputation in the business. The stronger the desire of the vendor in this regard, the better the after-purchase relationship will be. The CADD business is extremely competitive. Wise vendors know that wise buyers will communicate with past clients before selecting a vendor. For this reason, it is essential that the after-purchase relationship between the vendor and buyer be a positive one. The key is for buyers to determine how serious a vendor is about its reputation and image *before* dealing with it. This is the subject of the next section.

EVALUATING CADD VENDORS

Most people prefer to buy a car from a dealer with a longstanding track record, a good reputation, and a proven commitment to the after-purchase relationship. This is a wise approach. A similar approach is advisable when converting to CADD. In the previous section, the turnkey approach to implementation was recommended. This section explains how to evaluate turnkey vendors, their services, their training, and their after-purchase commitment.

Vendor Evaluation Criteria

In making an evaluation, the key is knowing what questions to ask and what criteria to use. The performance of a given CADD system is important—possibly the most important criterion. However, don't make the mistake of selecting a vendor solely on the weight of its system's performance. This point is best illustrated with the example of an automobile.

When purchasing a car, you look for one that performs well, of course. However, you also want one that is in your price range for which service and replacement parts are readily available and for which the dealer has a good reputation. The car that you end up buying will be the one that is the best compromise after you have considered all of these factors. The best-performing car in the world will be of little value if it cannot be quickly and reasonably repaired when it inevitably breaks down. The same rules apply in purchasing a CADD system.

The integrity, credibility, dependability, and fiscal soundness of the vendor are at least as important as the performance of its system. Before purchasing a CADD system from a given vendor, a buyer should take the time to get to know the vendor. It's much like a marriage. You don't really know your mate or your vendor until after the honeymoon is over.

What follows is an annotated list of criteria that can be used in evaluating vendors.

What is the nature of feedback from other companies that have dealt with the vendor?

Ask the vendor to supply a list of other clients and contact people in their companies. Find out if the vendor is considered honest and dependable and if it has a stable group of people to deal with. It's difficult to build the type of positive relationship with vendor representatives that is needed if the representatives continually change due to turnover.

Does the vendor have a written statement of its philosophy concerning the vendor/buyer relationship?

Know the official policy of the vendor so you have something to measure actual performance against. Show this written policy to other clients, and ask them to compare it to the actual performance they have experienced.

How long has the vendor been in the CADD business, and how committed is it to staying in the business?

It is important for the vendor to have a track record for you to judge. This is especially true for companies that are not familiar with CADD. A good rule of thumb is to let the more-experienced CADD users take their chances with new and unproven CADD vendors. A well-established track record is an indication that the vendor plans to stay in business.

Is the vendor fiscally sound?

The list of well-intended vendors that got into the CADD business with an excellent product line but did not have the financial wherewithall to make it through bad times is lengthy. No matter how good the system is, it will be of little use to you if the vendor that manufactures and markets it goes out of business. Consider the plight of the individuals who purchased DeLorean cars. Before seriously getting down to business with a vendor, ask your financial people to run a Dun and Bradstreet search on it (they will know what it is and how to do it). The vendor can also be asked to provide proof of its fiscal soundness. If this method is used, make sure that any data submitted are examined by competent, qualified financial experts.

How does the vendor handle service and maintenance calls?

Is there a toll-free number for making service complaints? Does the vendor contract with local technicians, or must they be transported from a central location? If they must be transported, what is the response time and how does it affect the cost?

Does the vendor express an interest in working with you to clearly identify your company's needs to ensure that its system will meet your needs?

A reputable vendor will turn down a sale before it will sell to a buyer whose needs it cannot reasonably meet. Find out from the vendor what percentage of its total installations are in applications similar to yours.

Is the vendor willing to participate in side-by-side comparisons with other vendors?

Vendors make it their business to know the strengths and weaknesses of the competition. A great deal can be learned about vendors and their products in side-by-side comparisons with other vendors. It's like inviting two or three insurance sales representatives to sit down at the kitchen table with you and compare policies. They will make sure to ask questions that you might not have thought of.

Does the vendor provide complete installation, startup, testing, and debugging services?

A vendor should provide the same type of service you expect when buying a new car. A reputable dealer wouldn't ask you to uncrate the car, tune the engine, perform all of the dealer preparation tasks, and fill it with gas; nor should a CADD vendor. Installation services should include, at least, the following:

Unpacking and setup
Inventory of components to ensure that everything has been shipped
Hardware setup and testing
Software installation, trial runs, and debugging
Establishing networking interfaces
Familiarization of the buyer with all technical manuals
Periodic spot-checking after installation

How comprehensive are the training services provided?

The success of a CADD conversion depends on the acceptance, skills, and creativity of people involved at all levels. These things will depend on the quality of the training provided. If managers receive the type of training needed, they will be able to handle the CADD conversion in a way that will ensure its acceptance among employees. If employees receive the proper training, they will have the skills and creativity on the system that are necessary to make it really pay for itself. Some training services to look for include:

Pre-installation management training
Pre-installation familiarization of all employees
Pre-installation training of key employees
Post-installation training at the beginning and advanced levels
Post-installation training on an advanced level for managers

SELECTING A CADD SYSTEM

Now that you know how to evaluate potential vendors, you are almost ready to get down to the business of evaluating the CADD systems of these vendors; but first, two preliminary tasks must be completed:

1. Examine your design and drafting operation and make a list of the types of design and drafting needs your company has (e.g., analysis, review, modelling, working drawings, bills of material).
2. Using the criteria set forth above, compile a list of vendors that might be able to meet these needs and with which you would feel comfortable doing business. Narrow the list to a workable number, and then begin examining the systems of these vendors in detail.

The following CADD System Selection Checklist is designed to help you evaluate individual CADD systems before making a decision about which to purchase.

CADD SYSTEM SELECTION CHECKLIST

Vendor _____
System Name _____

Hardware Considerations

1. What type of processor technology is the system based on?
   _____ 8 bit   _____ 32 bit
   _____ 12 bit   _____ 36 bit
   _____ 24 bit

2. Who manufactures the processor?
   _____ IBM
   _____ Data General
   _____ Digital Equipment Corporation (DEC)
   _____ Hewlett-Packard
   _____ Prime
   _____ Other (specify)_____

3. What type of graphics display is used?
   _____ Raster   _____ Single
   _____ Storage   _____ Color
   _____ Refresh   _____ Monochrome
   _____ Dual   _____ Gray

4. Does the system use a separate text terminal?
   _____ Yes
   _____ No

5. Are cursor control devices used?
   _____ Puck   _____ Thumbwheels
   _____ Tablet   _____ Joystick
   _____ Light pen   _____ Trackball

6. Are output devices used or available as options?
   _____ Pen plotter (size options_____)
   _____ Electrostatic plotter
   _____ Photoplotter
   _____ Impact printer
   _____ Dot matrix printer
   _____ Electrostatic hardcopy unit

Software Considerations

1. What types of software packages are available?
   _____ General drafting
   _____ Mechanical design and drafting
   _____ Architectural design and drafting
   _____ Electronic design and drafting

_____ Structural design and drafting
_____ Civil engineering and drafting
_____ Education and training
_____ Technical publications
_____ Mapping
_____ Solids modelling
_____ Mechanical manufacturing
_____ Electronic manufacturing
_____ Technical manuals
_____ Training manuals
_____ Maintenance logs
_____ Audio-visual training materials

2. What symbols libraries are available?

_____ General drafting   _____ Structural drafting
_____ Mechanical drafting   _____ Civil drafting
_____ Architectural drafting   _____ Mapping
_____ Electronic drafting

3. What types of menu options are available?

_____ Tablet
_____ Screen
_____ Keyboard or push-button

4. What are the basic graphics commands available to users?

_____ Point   _____ Ellipse
_____ Solid line   _____ Planes
_____ Hidden line   _____ Surfaces of revolution
_____ Dashed line   _____ Fillets
_____ Construction line   _____ Rounds
_____ Centerline   _____ Individual arrowhead
_____ Circle   _____ Ruled surfaces
_____ Arc   _____ Meshes
_____ Irregular curve
_____ Crosshatching (options)_____
_____ Others (specify)_____

5. What manipulation functions are available to users?

_____ Move   _____ Stretch

_____ Rotate   _____ Pan
_____ Copy   _____ Step
_____ Zoom in   _____ Mirror
_____ Others (specify)_____

6. What modification commands are available to users?
   _____ Edit
   _____ Erase
   _____ Delete
   _____ Insert
   _____ Redraw
   _____ Others (specify)_____

7. What facilitation commands are available to users?
   _____ File
   _____ Library
   _____ Others (specify)_____

8. What output commands are available to users?
   _____ Plot
   _____ Print
   _____ Copy
   _____ Others (specify)_____

After-Purchase Considerations

1. What is the warranty period for hardware?_____
2. What is the warranty period for software?_____
3. Is a hardware maintenance contract available?
   _____ Yes
   _____ No
   _____ Cost (specify)_____
   _____ Period (specify)_____

4. Is a software maintenance contract available?
   _____ Yes
   _____ No
   _____ Cost (specify)_____
   _____ Period (specify)_____

5. Is there a single source for maintenance and repair of all hardware components?

_____ Yes

_____ No

6. Is there a toll-free number for maintenance problems?

_____ Yes

_____ No

7. What are the arrangements for software updates?

_____ Automatic updates supplied

_____ Supplied by contract only (annual fee)_____

Training Considerations

1. Is prepurchase training available?

_____ Yes

_____ No

_____ Where (specify)_____

_____ Cost (specify)_____

2. Is training available for managers?

_____ Yes

_____ No

_____ Where (specify)_____

_____ Cost (specify)_____

3. What training aids come with the system?

_____ Training manual   _____ Videotapes

_____ Films or filmstrips   _____ Workbooks

_____ Slide presentations

Miscellaneous Considerations

1. Delivery period for the system?_____
2. Is the system expandable for future updates and add-ons?

_____ Yes

_____ No

3. Is there a users' group of companies with the system?

_____ Yes

_____ No

_____ Membership fee (specify)_____

_____ Meets how often (specify)_____

_____ Meets where (specify)_____

HOW WILL CADD IMPLEMENTATION AFFECT THE COMPANY?

The immediate answer to this question is that CADD will have a different effect on different companies. A CADD conversion can succeed or fail. However, if managers planning and implementing the conversion understand the various ways CADD can impact their companies, they will be better able to ensure that the impact is positive.

What follows is a brief list of predictable effects that will have to be dealt with during the conversion.

The Learning Curve

Even the most expert designers and drafters who have been productive in a manual setting will be temporarily set back by the CADD conversion. Manual designers and drafters who accept CADD and want to learn can become proficient in three to six months. This means that managers must deal with productivity and workflow problems during the first three to six months after converting to a CADD operation. This can be handled in one of two ways:

1. Accept and plan for an initial drop in productivity and interruptions in the workflow.
2. Hire temporary CADD specialists to maintain productivity and the workflow while permanent employees are learning.

Even with the best training, the normal workflow will be interrupted during the CADD transition period. This can be a problem because better productivity and faster turnaround time on design and drafting projects were probably the "anchors" of your justification for getting into CADD in the first place. Temporary CADD specialists can help, but they add to the cost of the conversion. In any case, higher management must be made aware of what to expect during the first three to six months of the conversion.

Learning curve problems, productivity problems, and workflow problems can be expected and planned for. Another type of problem that should be planned for and dealt with openly and in straightforward terms is employee acceptance.

Employee acceptance is critical to the success of a CADD conversion. The good news is that experience has shown manual designers and drafters readily accept CADD after the job security question has been settled. Managers planning a CADD conversion should have a plan for the following:

1. Letting employees know—before installation—how the CADD conversion will affect their jobs.
2. Offering intercompany transfers for individuals who simply cannot adapt.
3. Offering early retirement plans for employees who are close to retirement and cannot adapt to CADD.

When employees know that their jobs are safe if they learn CADD and that reasonable alternatives exist for those who cannot or do not wish to, they will readily accept it and the transition will go smoothly.

Chapter 7
PLANNING, PRESENTING, AND
EVALUATING CADD TRAINING

One of the most important components of the CADD conversion is training. Unfortunately, training is the component that has received the least attention. In CADD development over the years, training has taken a back seat to hardware and software. Millions of dollars have been spent in the research and development departments of CADD vendors on developing better hardware and software. Much less has been spent on providing better training.

Educational institutions, due to financial limitations and the need to update teachers, have lagged behind in providing CADD training. Many technical schools, community colleges, colleges, and universities provide training in CADD, but these schools are considered pioneers in their states.

In order to sell CADD systems, vendors have found they must provide CADD training. For vendors, it's like Henry Ford trying to sell cars to a population that doesn't know how to drive. Some vendors have hired professional educators to assist with their CADD training programs and some have not. In many cases, training is handled by the marketing department. Of course, this approach can affect the quality of the training because marketing personnel know marketing, not education and training.

There is a critical need to improve and expand CADD training. This chapter is designed to help persons responsible for CADD training do just that. The first part of the chapter is for vendor personnel, and the second is for educational institutions.

This chapter is not intended for all readers. It has been included to help those noneducators who find themselves charged with the responsibility for preparing, presenting, and evaluating CADD training. This is a large group. Most CADD training takes place outside of a traditional educational setting. Drafting managers, vendor sales and marketing personnel, and many other persons with little or no formal teacher training are being given the responsibility for CADD training in their companies. This chapter was specially designed to provide these types of people with the background they need to ensure that the training they provide is optimally beneficial to recipients. However, drafting, design, engineering, and architectural practitioners may also find it helpful in developing an understanding of what they should expect in the way of training from a vendor or a school.

VENDOR-PROVIDED TRAINING

What do vendors need to know in order to provide the highest quality of training possible? Of course, they need to know all of the ins and outs of their systems, but much more is necessary for training. Many people think, "If I can do it, I can teach it." This is not necessarily so. To provide CADD training, one must know CADD and know it well, as a concept and from a technical perspective. But this is not enough. One must also know about teaching and learning. Vendors planning to provide training for buyers and potential buyers need to know such nontechnical information as:

1. What is learning?
2. What is teaching?
3. What are the most important principles of learning?
4. How do I put this together for a CADD training program?

These areas represent the foundation of understanding upon which a high-quality CADD training program can be built. Trying to provide such training without this understanding is like starting out on a long trip and not knowing where you are going or how to get there.

What Is Learning?

Learning can be best defined as a change in behavior that results from experience. The behavioral change can be physical and readily apparent, or it can be intellectual or attitudinal and not so readily apparent. There are three domains of learning that should be understood by training personnel:

1. The cognitive domain
2. The psychomotor domain
3. The affective domain

The **cognitive domain** has to do with mentally learning facts, figures, and information. You deal in this domain of learning when you teach buyers things such as the different types of plotters, the various types of software available, and the definition of "computer."

The **psychomotor domain** has to do with physical dexterity skills. You deal in this domain when you teach buyers how to perform operational tasks like cursor control, keyboard skills, digitizing, and loading the plotter.

The **affective domain** has to do with attitudes and personalities, the more intangible aspects of learning. You deal in this domain of learning when you try to help practicioners accept CADD and develop a positive attitude toward it. This domain of learning is one of the most important for vendors to be familiar with and should not be taken lightly.

In addition to the three domains of learning outlined above, vendor personnel should be familiar with three critical characteristics of learning:

Learning is purposeful. All learners have their reasons for becoming involved in a learning situation such as a CADD training program. People learn best when the learning relates to their purpose in becoming involved. Vendors should take the time to find out why each individual has become involved in the CADD training. Is he there because he wants to be? Is she there because the boss made her attend? Whatever the reason is, the learning should relate to that reason.

Learning comes from experience. People learn by doing, not by the teacher doing. Lecture, discussion, and demonstration are all important, but the real learning takes places when people experience what they are trying to learn. This concept is easy to understand if you think back to when you learned to ride a bicycle. Someone showed you the bicycle, told you about the different parts of the bicycle, and showed you how to ride it. At that point you did not know how to ride, as you soon learned when you tried for the first time. In order to really learn, you had to try to ride it, fall down, get back up, and try again. Through this experience, you eventually became skilled at riding a bicycle. The lecture and demonstration you received helped, but the real learning came from the doing.

Learning is an active process. This is why you can learn more from reading than from watching television. Reading is active. Watching television is passive, unless coupled with some related activities. Training personnel should not assume that people will remember something or be able to apply it simply because they have heard it. Learners must use what they are learning.

What is Teaching?

Books have been written on this subject, and doctoral dissertations that line library shelves contain mountains of data that attempt to answer this question. However, teaching is really a very simple concept if you understand learning, because teaching is just helping people learn. This is an important concept to grasp. **Teaching is helping people learn.** In order to do so, vendor personnel must understand several principles of learning and incorporate the results of this understanding into the preparation, presentation, application, and evaluation phases of their CADD training programs.

What are the Most Important Principles of Learning?

There are many principles of learning that could be listed by educational scholars; some are statements of the obvious, and some are less obvious. What follows is an annotated list of several principles with which vendor personnel should be familiar:

1. People learn best when they are ready to learn.
2. The more often people use what they learn, the better they understand it, in the case of knowledge, or the better they can do it, in the case of skills.
3. People retain learning better and want to learn more when they see the usefulness of the learning.
4. Learning new material or skills is easier if it can be built on old learning.
5. Learning must be accomplished in a step-by-step, systematic process.
6. Successful learning stimulates additional learning and motivates people to want to learn.
7. The sooner a person has the satisfaction of knowing that learning has taken place, the more ready he or she will be to take on new learning.

Each of these principles says something to vendor personnel about delivering the best possible training for buyers. The first principle—people learn best when they are ready to learn—means that training personnel should not dive right into training. They should give people time to get ready to learn. This means more than loosening up the class with a few jokes; it also means finding out why each student is present and what the students hope to get out of the training. It means ensuring up front that every learner understands how he or she can benefit personally from the learning. When people understand this, they will be ready to learn.

The second principle has to do with application. Students need to use what they learn. This means that training personnel must schedule the maximum amount of application time. Most people understand the application concept when dealing with skills. However, many do not understand application as it applies to learning knowledge and conceptual data. Application in these cases can be accomplished through open discussion, question-and-answer sessions, additional research into the subject, written activities such as reports and papers, and required presentations in front of the class.

The third principle has to do with the learners recognizing the usefulness of what they are attempting to learn. This principle relates somewhat to the first one. It is worth the effort of training personnel to spend time in every lesson relating this principle to the goals and needs of the learners. Beginning every lesson with "this is how you will use what you are about to learn" can motivate people to want to learn.

The fourth principle has to do with building new learning on old learning, an important principle to remember. Observing this rule will make the learning process flow smoothly. New learning can be confusing and even frightening to people. Basing it on old learning gives people a foundation of understanding to refer to when they become confused. Today's new learning becomes tomorrow's old learning and so on up the learning ladder.

The fifth principle is an extension of the fourth. It has to do with ensuring that learning takes place in a step-by-step fashion. This approach minimizes the confusion that is inherent in learning and ensures that the fourth principle of learning is observed. Training personnel ensure that learning takes place in a step-by-step fashion by planning. The entire training program should be planned sequentially, and learners should be aware of the scope and sequence of the learning that will take place.

The sixth principle has to do with stimulating additional learning through success. What this says to training personnel is structure the training so learners accomplish goals and objectives in a timely fashion and are aware they are doing so. This means several other things to training personnel:

1. There must be goals and objectives established for the CADD training program.
2. Learners must be aware of the goals and objectives.
3. Learners should see visual evidence of accomplishment of the goals and objectives, such as progress charts on which they are checked off.

4. Goals and objectives must be broken down far enough so learners do not have to work too long before seeing some accomplishment. Correspondingly, you don't want to break the goals and objectives down so far that they don't challenge the learner. Developing goals and objectives that meet these two criteria is both an art and a science.

The seventh principle is an extension of the sixth. It simply means there should be a system of documenting the accomplishment of goals. Providing learners with visual records of progress can be an excellent motivator for readying them for additional learning.

The Four-Step Teaching Approach

Now that you know what learning is, what teaching is, how they relate, and some important principles of learning, you are ready to see how to put these things to work in a CADD training program. One of the most effective methods for delivering training is the four-step approach to teaching and learning. The four steps are:

1. Preparation
2. Presentation
3. Application
4. Evaluation

Step 1—Preparation

Preparation is the planning step. The first planning task that must be accomplished is the overall plan for the CADD training program. This involves developing a comprehensive knowledge and skills outline, which is very much like the table of contents of a book. It contains the major topical headings that will be dealt with in the training and the subheadings for each major topic. In other words, it is an outline of what training personnel will teach and what learners will learn. It includes both knowledge and skills entries.

Developing a knowledge and skills outline will require some research and some brainstorming among people who know CADD and who know the needs of people who wish to learn about CADD. All efforts center around the question "What do manual practitioners need to learn to be competent CADD practitioners?"

Example 7–1

Knowledge and Skills Outline

Type of Training Program Computer-aided design and drafting

Level of Training Program Beginning level

Target Group For Training Drafters, designers, and engineers

Scope and Sequence

1. THE COMPUTER AS A CONCEPT
   "Computer" defined
   Classifications of computers
   Micros, minis, mainframes, and supercomputers
   Humans versus computers
   Components of a typical computer system
   Benefits of the computer
   Historical development of computers
   Applications of the computer

2. THE COMPUTER IN DRAFTING
   Historical development of drafting from T-squares to CADD
   CADD defined
   Impact of CADD on drafting and design
   Future outlook of drafting and design with regard to CADD
   CADD myths and realities
   The design process and how CADD affects it
   The drafting process and how CADD affects it
   A typical CADD system
   Functions of CADD system components

   Example 7–1 is page 1 of a 10-page knowledge and skills outline for a beginning-level CADD training program. Example 7–2 is page 9 of that same 10-page outline. Note that the entries on Example 7–1 are knowledge oriented and the entries on Example 7–2 are skills oriented.

   A complete knowledge and skills outline represents the overall picture of what is to be taught and learned in a CADD training program. Of course, each

Example 7–2   Page Number 9 of 10

Knowledge and Skills Outline

Type of Training Program __Computer-aided design and drafting__

Level of Training Program __Beginning__

Target Group for Training __Drafters, designers, and engineers__

24. GENERAL OPERATIONAL SKILLS
    Keyboard skills
    Cursor control
    Menu and submenu interaction
    Digitizing

25. TEXT CREATION AND INTERACTION
    Activating text options on menus and responding to prompts
    Entering text
    Modifying text
    Manipulating text

26. GRAPHICS CREATION
    Activating graphics options on menus and responding to prompts
    Creating graphic data
    Modifying graphic data
    Manipulating graphic data

27. SIZE SPECIFICATION
    Activating size specification options and responding to prompts
    Automatic dimensioning
    Leaders and callouts
    Modifying dimensional data

vendor should make the knowledge and skills outline specific to its systems and applications. With the knowledge and skills outline completed, you are ready to complete the final phase of planning: developing individual lesson plans.

The relationship of the knowledge and skills outline and lesson plans can be understood by relating it to a roadmap atlas of the United States. The knowledge and skills outline is the big map at the beginning that shows the entire country. It provides the big picture but does not provide all the details that will be needed for driving across country. The lesson plans are the individual state maps that are much more detailed. It is important to have both if you plan to drive across country. The same is true of the outline and lesson plans.

The knowledge and skills outline gives the big picture of the CADD training program. The individual lesson plans give the day-to-day details needed by vendor personnel actually delivering the training.

A lesson plan is a tool that answers several important questions for training personnel:

1. What are the name and subject matter of the lesson?
2. Where does the lesson fit into the overall training program?
3. What is the purpose of the lesson?
4. What are the learning objectives of the lesson?
5. How will the lesson be taught?
6. What training materials will be required?
7. How will learners be evaluated?
8. How will evaluation data be quantified and communicated to learners? (i.e., scores, grades, pass/fail, satisfactory/unsatisfactory)

The major topical headings on the knowledge and skills outline become the subjects of lessons. One topical heading might be one lesson; another heading might take two or even three lessons to cover adequately. Deciding how much to include in a given lesson is important. Remember the sixth principle of learning: "Successful learning stimulates additional learning . . ." This is where that principle comes to bear. Training personnel must decide how much to include in a lesson so the lesson is challenging enough to keep the learners interested but short enough for them to see some progress before they become bored or overwhelmed. Making these decisions accurately takes experience; there is no magic equation. Consequently, training personnel new to the game will find themselves revising lesson plans frequently until they develop a feel for the right amount of learning to attempt in a lesson.

Example 7–3 is a sample of a lesson plan format that will be helpful in developing lesson plans for CADD training. The first entry is the lesson's title. This should match a major subheading or a subheading on the knowledge and skills outline. The lesson number shows where the particular lesson fits into the total number of lessons in the CADD training program.

The "Statement of Purpose" is something that should be explained to learners at the beginning of the lesson. It says "This is the reason that you are

Example 7–3

Standard Lesson Plan Format

Lesson Title _____

Lesson number _____ of _____

Statement of Purpose

Learning Objectives
Upon completion of this lesson, students should be able to demonstrate proficiency in performing the following tasks:

Delivery System

Training Materials Required

Evaluation System

Reporting of Evaluation Results

studying this lesson." This ensures that the learners are trying to learn what the trainers are trying to teach.

The learning objectives are specific statements which show exactly what learners should be able to do after completing the lesson. Learners who know exactly what it is they are supposed to be learning are more likely to learn it. Teachers who have a well-defined list of what they are supposed to be teaching will be better able to stay on track and ensure that students are not led off on a nonproductive tangent. In addition, the objectives will help the teacher and the learners come back to the proper point of departure when the class does go off on a tangent.

The delivery system is the compilation of teaching and learning methods that will be used in presenting the lesson from the teacher's perspective or for satisfying the learning objectives from the learner's perspective. A delivery system might involve lecture and discussion, demonstration, and question-and-answer sessions. An explanation of the delivery system lets the teacher and the learners know how they will go about teaching and learning the lesson.

The training materials explanation should include a list of all materials that will be needed by the teacher and students, as well as who will provide the materials. This allows teachers to let students know ahead of time what materials they are responsible for bringing to training sessions. It also gives teachers prior warning of materials they will need to provide.

The evaluation system entry provides an explanation of how learners will be evaluated (i.e., tests, observation, peer consensus). Evaluation is a critical component. Employers will want to know how their employees performed in the CADD training program and whether they learned everything they will need to know to be productive with regard to CADD. Teachers also need to know if learning is taking place and to what degree. The evaluation component is dealt with later in this chapter.

The final entry deals with reporting evaluation results. There are a number of different methods for communicating the results of an evaluation (i.e., grades, scores, pass/fail statements, satisfactory/unsatisfactory statements). Students need to know before a lesson begins both how they will be evaluated and how the results of evaluations will be communicated and reported.

Example 7–4 shows a complete lesson plan developed from the first entry of the Knowledge and Skills Outline in Example 7–1. Examine all of the entries closely. This sample will give training personnel an idea of the extent of planning necessary to deliver top-quality CADD training for buyers. It will also give buyers an idea of what they should be able to expect with regard to training and the documentation of that training. It is a good idea for buyers to ask to see the documentation that vendors have available concerning the training they provide. Well-planned and well-presented documentation is an indication that the training will not be haphazard.

Example 7–4

Standard Lesson Plan Format

Lesson Title _____THE COMPUTER AS A CONCEPT_____

Lesson number _____1_____ of _____35_____

Statement of Purpose

The purpose of this lesson is to help practitioners develop a basic understanding of the computer as a concept. This understanding will form the basis for all additional learning in the area of computer-aided design and drafting for which an understanding of computers is essential.

Learning Objectives

Upon completion of this lesson, students should be able to demonstrate proficiency in performing the following tasks:

1. Stating orally a definition for the term "computer."
2. Listing four characteristics of the computer that set it apart from other machines.
3. Explaining the difference between "analog" and "digital" computers.
4. Describing micro, mini, mainframe, and supercomputers in terms of their makeup.
5. Explaining the relationship of micros, minis, mainframes, and supers.
6. Explaining how humans and computers differ in terms of their strengths and weaknesses.
7. Explaining how humans and computers complement each other in terms of strengths and weaknesses.
8. Listing the various components of a typical computer system and the functions of each.
9. Listing the various types of computer software and the functions of each.
10. Listing the benefits of computers in terms of work and productivity.
11. Explaining benchmarks in the development of computers from the beginning until the present.
12. Listing at least 10 applications of the computer.

Delivery System

The teaching and learning will involve a presentation by the instructor supported by overhead transparencies and chalkboard interaction. Students are expected to participate in a teacher-directed discussion as well as a question-and-answer period. Students should take copious notes.

Training Materials Required

Teacher Materials: Set of overhead transparencies on THE COMPUTER
                      AS A CONCEPT
                      Chalk
                      Overhead projector and screen
                      Pointer

Student Materials: Pencils or pens
                    Composition notebook

Evaluation System

At the conclusion of the lesson, the teacher will administer an objective test covering all of the information presented in the lesson.

Reporting of Evaluation Results

Tests will be scored as a percentage of correct answers accomplished compared with total possible correct answers. The scores will be recorded on each test. A score of 75% or higher will be considered passing. Students scoring less than 75% will be given an outside-of-class assignment and additional instruction, and be allowed to retake the test until their scores reach 75% or better.

Step 2—Presentation

The second step of the four-step teaching approach is **Presentation**. Presentation is the step in which the lessons planned are actually delivered. There are a number of effective ways for presenting instruction. The most effective method in a given situation depends on what is being taught. If the lesson involves knowledge development, lecture/discussion can be effective. If the lesson involves skills development, demonstration can be effective.

Lecture/discussion and demonstration are the two most widely used presentation methods and, if used properly, they can be very effective. Both methods will work in a traditional setting such as a classroom, a workshop, or a seminar. In these formats, lectures and demonstrations are presented by teachers to a group of learners. All learners are required to progress at the same rate—the rate of the group. Both methods will also work in the less-traditional, self-paced situation in which lectures are presented on videotapes or through computer-assisted instruction packages, and demonstrations are presented on videotapes or some other form of telecommunications technology.

The traditional approach is best for moving groups of 10 or more through the training program. The self-paced approach is effective for dealing with smaller numbers or individuals who must begin the training program at different times. In either approach—traditional or self-paced—the same rules apply in presenting a lecture and a demonstration. Vendor personnel involved in training or expecting to become involved should be familiar with these rules.

The key to giving an effective lecture is "tell 'em what you are going to tell 'em, then tell 'em, then tell 'em what you told 'em." This old adage is a wise rule of thumb. It means that a good lecture has an introduction, a body, and a conclusion. Too many people approach a lecture as if it were a sermon or a broadcast. It is neither. A lecture is a structured, carefully planned instruction delivery method that can be very effective for teaching groups in a traditional classroom, workshop, or seminar setting.

Example 7–5 is a lecture model that contains a breakdown of the major points that training personnel should be attentive to in preparing and delivering

Example 7–5

Lecture Model

Introduction

Greet the group and put everyone at ease.
Establish credibility with an overview of credentials.
State the topic of the lecture.
Explain the purpose of the lecture.
List the learning objectives of the lecture.
Explain how the lecture relates to past learning.
Give definitions for new terms contained in the lecture.

Body

Present the lecture material in an organized, step-by-step manner.
Answer questions from the group as they arise, but keep learners on course.

Conclusion

Restate the topic of the lecture.
Restate the purpose of the lecture.
Restate the learning objectives.
Restate the major points.
Make concluding statements.
Issue a final call for questions from the group.
Release the group or direct them to the next activity as appropriate.

lectures. In the introduction, instructors should greet the group and spend a few minutes establishing credibility.

The greeting should put the group at ease. Humor is an effective tool in this regard. The overview of your credentials should help establish you as a person to be respected in the field in question. This is important. People learn better from someone they respect. The fastest and most effective way to establish respect is through a rundown of pertinent credentials. The best way to keep respect is to live up to your credentials by presenting a well-prepared, thoroughly researched, well-organized lecture.

The next component of the introduction is the statement of purpose. In this component, the lecturer explains the overall purpose of the lecture so learners know what to expect. It's like reading the short description in the *TV Guide* before watching a program: If you know a little about what to expect, you will be in a better position to absorb it. This also applies to learners participating as listeners in a lecture.

The next component of the introduction is the statement of the learning objectives. This component takes the next step in expounding on the statement of purpose. The list of learning objectives tells learners exactly what they are supposed to learn during the lecture. Sharp learners will copy down each objective as a major heading for taking notes. Sharp lecturers will require them to do so.

Taking the time to state the purpose of the lecture and to outline the learning objectives is like sitting down before a trip and going over the itinerary and map. It lets everyone know where they are going, why they are going, and when they should get there.

The next component of the introduction involves explaining how this lecture relates to past learning. This helps satisfy an important principle of learning which specifies that new learning should be built on old learning. It also helps orient learners by letting them know how and where the lecture in question fits in.

The final component of the introduction involves presenting definitions for any terms that are included in the lecture with which the learners may not be familiar. Wise lecturers will even have students take down the definitions in their notes for additional reinforcement. This combination is more likely to lead to learning than just hearing the definitions.

Once the seven components in the introduction have been accomplished, the lecturer can move on to the body of the lecture. This is the part most people associate with lectures. However, those training personnel who take the time to present a structured, comprehensive introduction will find that their effort will pay off in increased understanding and learning.

In the introduction to the lecture, you present the skeleton. In the body you fill in the rest. Each point outlined in the introduction should be treated in depth in the body of the lecture and in the order outlined in the introduction. During the lecture it is important to stay on track and proceed in the order that learners are expecting. There is nothing wrong with going off on a brief tangent if it relates to the topic of the lecture. However, tangents should be identified as such so students don't become confused trying to determine whether to take notes and, if so, where the tangent material fits in.

Some lecturers do not allow questions during the lecture, but this can be a mistake. The best time to ask a question, from a learner's point of view, is when it arises. Learning may be served by allowing students to ask questions during the body of the lecture. In fact, many educators call this method the "lecture/discussion" method and use it effectively to involve learners and to keep them interested.

The only time a lecturer should not respond to a question is when the material the question refers to will be dealt with later in the lecture. If one learner has a question, chances are good that several others have the same question but are afraid to ask.

Questions asked during the body of the lecture can lead to interesting and profitable discussion among group members. The lecturer should encourage this. It will enhance interest and learning by making the lecture an active, participatory process rather than a passive activity. When discussion does grow out of questions, it is the lecturer's responsibility to keep it on track and ensure that questions and the resulting discussion are germane to the lecture topic. When someone begins to get off track, the lecturer should gently guide discussion back to the topic of the lecture.

Once the body of the lecture has been accomplished, the lecturer should present a comprehensive conclusion. This is an important component of the lecture: "Tell 'em what you told 'em." To many lecturers, this seems redundant, and it is—purposely so. Redundancy enhances learning. Additionally, what might be redundant to a lecturer who is an expert and has heard it many times before is still new to learners who might have just heard it for the first time in the lecture.

The first step in the conclusion is to restate the topic of the lecture. The second step is to restate the purpose of the lecture. By restating the purpose of the lecture, you give the learners a chance to ask themselves, "Did the lecture satisfy its purpose for me?" If it didn't, there is still a chance to ask questions.

The next step is to restate the learning objectives. Again, this gives learners an opportunity to ask themselves if the planned learning has actually taken place or if questions need to be answered. The next step is to restate the major points made in the lecture. This is nothing more than a brief summary, but it can be valuable in allowing learners to fill in missing information in their notes.

The next step is to make a concluding statement to wrap everything up. With this done, issue a final call for questions. This final call is a last opportunity for all learners to make sure that their questions have been asked and answered, to make sure their notes are complete, and to ask for clarification on any information that may still be fuzzy.

The Lecture Model in Example 7–5 can improve your lectures significantly by itself if all steps are followed every time a lecture is presented, no matter how many times it is presented. A lecturer is like an actor who stars in a long-running stage play. No matter how many times the play is presented, it must be approached as if it is the first time every time because, to the viewer, it is. The same is true of lectures.

In addition to following the guidelines set forth in Example 7–5, there are several other ways to improve the organization and quality of lectures. One has already been mentioned briefly: **discussion.** By actually prompting and facilitating discussion during the body of a lecture, lecturers get the learners involved. The importance of this technique cannot be overstated. It is a form of applying what is being learned. And as you have already seen, application is a fundamental part of the learning process.

Discussion also allows students to learn from each other. In any given group, a multitude of interests, abilities, and experiences can be found. By promoting discussion that is germane to the lecture topic, the lecturer will bring these factors into play to the benefit of all learners as well as himself. There is no teacher living that did not learn something from every group of students taught.

Another way to improve lectures is through the use of many **visual aids.** If students see as well as hear and discuss, they will be more likely to retain what is being presented. There are numerous different types of visual aids, ranging from the old-fashioned to the ultramodern. All of the various types of visual aids can be used effectively to enhance a lecture.

However, visual aids should not just be used as eyewash. Every aid used should serve a clearly defined purpose. Some of the more effective visual aids for use with lectures are chalkboards or their more modern equivalents that use markers; overhead transparencies; slides; flip charts; and handouts.

An effective technique is to outline the introduction to the lecture on some form of visual aid (e.g., on the chalkboard, on a flip chart, or on a handout). This gives the learner a visual record of what is going to take place and in what order. It also will help guide the learner through the lecture and provide a way of keeping notetaking and thinking on track as the lecture progresses.

In addition, each major point covered in a lecture should be supported by some type of visual aid. This is where overhead transparencies and slides can be very effective. A visual aid emphasizes an important point and helps learners form a mental image of that point. It is this mental image that they will conjure up later when trying to remember that particular point from the lecture.

Even the best-researched, best-organized, best-presented lecture can go flat if the lecturer is not adept at verbal and nonverbal communications as they relate lectures. Following is an annotated list of communication techniques with which training personnel should be familiar:

Proper use of notes. A lecture should *never* be read to a group. Nothing is more boring than to sit and listen to another person read. Intelligent learners will say to themselves, "If all he is going to do is read, he could just give us the script and we'll read it ourselves." A lecturer should have an annotated outline but should refer to it only sparingly as a way of marking progress and keeping on track.

Enthusiasm. The importance of enthusiasm cannot be overstated. Enthusiasm is contagious! If a speaker is excited about the subject, before long the learners will be too. Once a group is excited about what is being learned, half the battle is won. Enthusiasm is just that, however. It does not mean that a speaker should become overly excited or so hyperactive as to remind the learners of a cheap television commercial.

Hand and arm movement. This is a form of nonverbal communication that can be very important. Avoid movements such as crossing the arms or putting hands in pockets and jingling change. Besides being distracting, they tell the learners you are insecure, and insecure is the last thing you want to appear to be in front of a group that is supposed to look upon you as the expert. Hand and arm movement should be used and timed properly to emphasize important points or to accentuate information that is critical.

Body movement. One famous speaker, when asked why he moved around so much on the platform, responded, "Because it's harder to hit a moving target!" I hope you won't have to move around for this reason when lecturing, but you should move. A completely stationary lecturer can become like a statue. Body movement keeps learners awake and involved. By moving among the group, you can make the learning environment more personal. Just standing close to a loudmouth can quiet the person.

Eye contact. There are two times when you should definitely look a person right in the eyes: when shaking his or her hand and when presenting a lecture. Each time a lecturer makes eye contact, the receiver feels as if the lecturer is talking to him. Every time a lecturer looks at a person while giving a lecture, that person feels more like a participant.

Eye movement. Eye movement goes hand-in-hand with eye contact. All people in the group should be looked at while lecturing, not just one or a few friendly faces. When lecturing to a group, the speaker's eyes should constantly, but naturally, scan back and forth across the group.

Volume of voice. Two things will turn off a learner faster than anything when listening to a lecture: (1) someone who cannot be heard and (2) someone who is too loud. The first thing a lecturer should do is test the audio, whether using a microphone or speaking without amplification. Say a few words and determine the proper sound level for reading the entire audience without blasting anyone's eardrums.

Tone and pitch of voice. Every person who has attended any type of school has had the unfortunate experience of sitting through a dull, monotone lecture. Nothing is worse. Even the most exciting subject is hard to follow when presented in a boring, monotonous voice. The same is true of squeaky, whiny, or overly nasal tones of voice. Any person involved in presenting lectures should tape his or her voice frequently and listen. Most people are surprised to hear how they actually sound on tape; we often sound a great deal different than we think we do. Tone and pitch problems, if they exist, can be solved if the speaker will simply listen to them on tape and make a concerted effort to overcome them.

Clarity, diction, and choice of words. Listeners will be trying to take notes. Consequently, it is important to speak clearly and distinctly. Slurred or run-together words are difficult to understand. Make sure you know the words that you use in a lecture, as well as their proper pronunciation. Then use the proper pronunciation. Avoid slang or words that might be used in casual conversation with friends but not in front of a group of learners.

These various criteria are summarized in Example 7–6, a special critique sheet that can be used for evaluating the communication aspects of a lecturer's presentation. It is a good idea to ask a colleague to sit through one of your lectures and critique it using Examples 7–6 and 7–5. This evaluation process can be of considerable assistance in improving the communication and organizational aspects of your lectures.

Another evaluation technique that works well is to videotape your lecture and then critique it yourself. This is even more effective than having someone else critique your lectures because there is no denying what you see on the videotape.

The second technique that is used as much as the lecture in the presentation step of the four-step teaching approach is the **Demonstration**. Demonstrations are the appropriate method for teaching skills development. In other words, this is how training personnel teach learners how to operate CADD systems.

Regardless of whether the demonstration is given live or on videotape, there are certain considerations with which the demonstrator should be familiar. The lecture model in Example 7–5 can also be used for structuring a dem-

Example 7–6

Lecture Critique Sheet

Lecturer's Name _____

Lecture Topic _____

Directions

Review the criteria below before listening to the lecture. While listening to the lecture, rate the speaker's performance according to each criteria on a scale of 1 to 5. Five should be considered excellent and one should be considered poor.

_____ Proper use of notes

_____ Enthusiasm

_____ Hand and arm movement

_____ Body movement

_____ Eye contact

_____ Eye movement

_____ Volume of voice

_____ Tone and pitch of voice

_____ Clarity and diction

_____ Choice of words

Comments

_____

_____

_____

_____

_____

_____

onstration. Demonstrations have three parts: an introduction, a body, and a conclusion.

In the introduction of a demonstration, the instructor should follow established criteria similar to those set forth for lectures in Example 7–5:

Greet the group and put everyone at ease.

Establish credibility with an overview of credentials.

State the topic of the demonstration.

Explain the purpose of the demonstration.

List the learning objectives of the demonstration.

Explain how the demonstration related to past learning if it does (it should at least relate to a lecture the learners have listened to).

In the body of the demonstration, the instructor should present all steps slowly, deliberately, and in the proper sequence with corresponding explanations. Students should be allowed to stop the instructor and ask him or her to repeat procedures that are unclear as the demonstration progresses.

In the conclusion to a demonstration, the instructor should restate the purpose of the demonstration and the learning objectives so learners can gauge what they have actually learned against what they were supposed to learn. Students should also be given a last chance to ask questions or to have procedures repeated that are unclear.

Example 7–7 is a Skills Demonstration Critique Sheet that can be used to evaluate demonstrations. As with lectures, it is a good idea either to ask a colleague to critique your demonstrations or to have a demonstration videotaped so you can critique it yourself. In either case, the Skills Demonstration Critique Sheet will be helpful. Each criterion listed will help training personnel improve demonstrations. These criteria are listed below along with brief explanations:

Positioning the Group. It is the demonstrator's responsibility to position all learners so they can see the demonstration. This may require rearranging the room and shuffling people around, but it is essential that everyone be able to see and some people are too polite to correct the problem themselves.

Eliminate Distractions. Before starting a demonstration, eliminate anything that might distract the learners' attention. A noisy hallway problem can be solved by closing the door. Whatever distractions exist should be eliminated before attempting to present the demonstration. Don't try to compete with a distraction. It won't work.

Perform the Demonstration Slowly. Experts in operating a CADD system can whiz right through the various procedures, but learners must take things more slowly. It is important to use slow, deliberate movements in demonstrating operational procedures. Learners need to be able to readily see each individual step in a procedure.

Allow Questions During the Demonstration. Just as in giving a lecture, it is important to let learners ask questions as they arise. If they are forced to wait, one of two things will happen—both negative in terms of learning: (1) The

Example 7–7

Skills Demonstration Critique Sheet

Demonstrator's Name _____

Demonstration Topic _____

Directions

Write the word "yes" or "no" in the blanks that precede each criterion as appropriate. If you do not feel a given criterion applies in a certain situation, write "N/A."

General Considerations
_____ Positioned the group so everyone could easily see the demonstration.
_____ Eliminated all distracting influences in the area.
_____ Performed demonstration slowly enough to be understood.
_____ Allowed questions during the demonstration.
_____ Summarized at the end of the demonstration.

Explanation Considerations
_____ Kept explanations short and simple.
_____ Used simple language in giving explanations.
_____ Explained technical terms each time used.
_____ Repeated explanations if they were not understood.
_____ Related explanations to lecture material that preceded the demonstration.

Questioning Considerations
_____ Drew the group out using questions.
_____ Did not allow one person to dominate all questions.
_____ Did not call undue attention to incorrect answers.
_____ Asked questions in the same sequence as the demonstration sequence.

Comments
_____
_____
_____

learner will be so interested in his question that he will not be attentive to the demonstration or (2) The learner will forget the question.

Summarize at the End of the Demonstration. A demonstration should be summarized just like a lecture. This gives learners a last chance to clarify any remaining misunderstandings and to have procedures repeated. It also gives the demonstrator a chance to run through a mental checklist to make sure everything has been covered.

Keep Explanations Short and Simple. Operating a CADD system is not a complex undertaking. Consequently, explanations that accompany physical movements should not be complex. Short, simple explanations that are illustrated with actual physical movements are the easiest to follow and understand. Resist the urge to wander into a long, drawn-out philosophical explanation of how to control the screen cursor. Keep it simple.

Use Simple Language. Choose words that the learners will understand in giving explanations. The terminology that goes with CADD will be new to most learners. Use the correct terms during an explanation, but explain them as they are used and do so in the simplest terms possible. Avoid the urge to show off. Learning, not impressing learners with your vocabulary, is the goal of the demonstration.

Explain Technical Terms. CADD does have a language of its own, and many of the terms must necessarily be used in giving a CADD demonstration. However, these terms are usually new to experienced manual practitioners. Therefore, each time a technical term must be used, it should be explained.

Repeat Explanations. It can be irritating to demonstrators to re-explain a concept they have just explained. But consider this something that goes with the territory. It's all new to learners and at times will be just too much to grasp the first time around. It is said that patience is a virtue. Maybe; maybe not. But it is a helpful teaching tool.

Explanations Related to Lecture Material. Usually a demonstration is preceded by a lecture. When this is the case, demonstration material should be related to the lecture material where appropriate. This has two advantages: it builds new learning on old, and it provides continuity of learning.

Draw the Group Out with Questions. A demonstration that follows a lecture gives the instructor an opportunity to reaffirm the lecture material and enhance the demonstration. This is done by drawing people out through questions such as, "How does this procedure I am demonstrating relate to the lecture material?" or "How does this CADD procedure relate to how you perform the same task manually?" Such questions will involve learners in the demonstration and keep them interested.

Do Not Let One Student Dominate. On occasion there will be one learner who will, whether knowingly or not, dominate the questions/answer part of a demonstration. Such a person can turn other learners off and keep them from asking their questions. Demonstrators should make a point of drawing all participants into the demonstration rather than letting one dominate.

Do Not Call Attention to Incorrect Answers. If bells go off every time a learner incorrectly answers a question, soon questions won't be answered. All questions and corresponding responses should be dealt with in a positive way so learners will not feel inhibited about asking or attempting an answer.

Ask Questions in Sequence. In using questions to draw students out and keep them involved in a demonstration, make sure the questions match the procedure at hand. Don't get out of sequence. This tends to confuse learners and breaks the continuity of learning.

Step 3—Application

As soon as possible after a demonstration, all learners should be given the opportunity to try what has been demonstrated. At this point, it is critical that training personnel monitor their attempts closely. Skills are developed through repetition and become habit. Consequently, it is important to correct improperly accomplished procedures *before* they become habits. This is Step 3 of the four-step teaching approach. It's known as **application** and might be the most important step.

If learning CADD is like learning to ride a bicycle, application is that point when you get on for the first time and try to ride. You will make mistakes. You will fall down. But if someone is there to pick you up, dust you off, and show you what you did wrong, before long you will be riding on your own. The same is true in operating a CADD system.

Step 4—Evaluation

Evaluation is the step in which you find out how much learning has taken place and, indirectly, how much teaching. Most people associate evaluation with testing, but this is a misconception. Testing is one *method* of evaluating learning. There are several others also. As a vendor, it is important to evaluate learners, but it is equally important to have the learners evaluate you. In this way, you can constantly improve on shortcomings in your CADD training program.

Training personnel should be familiar with the following types of evaluation methods:

Objective written tests   Skills testing
Subjective written tests   Learner evaluation of instruction
Group testing

Before learning the essentials of each of these evaluation methods, training personnel should be familiar with several characteristics of tests.

Tests Should Be Valid. This means that a test should test what it was intended to test, not other factors. The best way to ensure that a test is valid is to develop it directly from the learning objectives for the lesson in question. If a test is to cover the material learned in lesson 5, develop the test question from the learning objectives for test 5.

Tests Should Be Reliable. This means a test should yield basically the same results if administered to similar groups. If one group is trained and tested this week and another next week, the results should be similar if the test used is reliable. One way to ensure reliability is to again use the learning objectives for the lesson in question. Another way is to increase the number of test questions. Generally speaking, the more questions, the greater the reliability.

Tests Should Be Easy to Administer and Score. A well-planned, well-developed test will be easy to administer and score. Both of these factors are important. The easier a test is to administer and score, the faster the test results can be gotten into the hands of the learners. Immediate feedback is the ideal in terms of letting learners know how well they have performed on a test.

It is poor practice to begin new learning without having tested the old learning. Well-developed test instruments allow testing to take place without slowing the process.

Tests Should Match the Activity. This is important. You don't test a learner's skills in operating a CADD system using a written test. On the other hand, you don't test lecture material using a skills test. Generally speaking, material covered in a lecture would be tested using either objective or subjective written tests. Operational skills developed as the result of a demonstration and corresponding application activities would be tested using a skills test.

These characteristics apply to all types of tests. Let's now examine the various types of tests, as well as other types of evaluations.

Objective Written Tests. Objective written tests require definite right or wrong answers. They are called *objective* because they are structured to allow no room for judgment or debate. An answer is either right or wrong. Objective tests are indicated when you want to test for recall or recognition of facts, figures, and other types of hard data.

A **recall test** requires that the learner recall a fact, figure, or some other brief answer from memory. Recall test items require either short answers or fill-in-the-blank responses. Examples of recall test items are:

1. What was the name of the first computer developed for commercial use?

   _____

2. List three types of plotters used in modern CADD systems.

   _____

   _____

   _____

In both of the examples above, learners must recall the answers from memory. Recall test items are the more difficult of the two types of objective test items. The easier of the two is the **recognition test** item. With this test, learners need only recognize the correct answer or a true statement from a false one.

Recognition test items include multiple choice, matching, and true-false, such as the following examples:

1. What component in a CADD system would be considered the "brains" of the system?
   A. The plotter
   B. The digitizer
   C. The processor
   D. The graphics terminal

A. Plotter   F. Keyboard
B. Digitizer   G. Applications software
C. Graphics terminal   H. Processor
D. Light pen   I. Printer
E. Thumbwheels   J. Menu

_____ 1. Device which outputs hardcopy of graphic data.
_____ 2. The "brains" of the system.
_____ 3. Device which outputs softcopy of graphic data.
_____ 4. Used to move the cursor in horizontal and
           vertical steps.
_____ 5. Device for outputting alphanumeric data.

True or False: The digitizer is a cursor control device shaped
like a fountain pen or a pocket flashlight.

The first example was a multiple choice recognition item. The learner need only examine the list and circle the correct response once it is recognized. The second example is five matching recognition items. Students match the correct responses from the ten possible with the five questions. Notice that in matching questions, the list of possible responses should contain several more choices than the number of questions. This rules out answering by process of elimination. The final example is a true-false item. With this type, learners need only recognize the statement as being either true or false.

All of the examples—recall and recognition—are objective test items. There is no room for error. The answers given are either right or wrong. These types of test items are the easiest to administer and score. They are appropriate for testing the learner's recall or recognition of facts, figures, and other hard data.

Subjective Written Tests. Objective tests will not test for understanding. They are used for testing the who, what, when, and where types of learning. What they will not test is why. "Why" requires more than recall and recognition; it requires understanding. In these cases, subjective test items are used. Subjective tests are sometimes called "essay tests." This is a bit of a misnomer because one doesn't have to write an essay on a subject to show she understands it. However, length is not the issue here. A text item is subjective because there is room for subjectivity in determining if the answer is right or wrong.

An example of a subjective question that could be answered in a paragraph or in 20 pages is:

Attack or defend the following statement: "CADD is better than
manual design and drafting."

Obviously, there could be a wide variety of responses to this question, and whether an answer is right or wrong will depend on the outlook of the person scoring the test. This is because "better" is a subjective word.

Generally speaking, objective tests are more appropriate for use by vendors in CADD training programs. Subjective testing on CADD issues is better left to the academics.

Group Testing. This may be the best evaluation method to use in vendor-provided CADD training programs, workshops, and seminars. With this method, training personnel develop a list of questions that have short, objective answers.

After the lecture and discussion, the questions are posed of the group, one at a time. A learner can only answer one question. This ensures that one bright learner doesn't dominate. A good rule of thumb is to have enough questions to ask everyone one or more.

Keep track of the number answered properly and the number missed. If the group scores 85% or better, the group passes the test. This can be an effective testing method for taking the pressure off individuals while allowing training personnel to get an idea of how well the training and learning are going.

TRAINING PROVIDED BY EDUCATIONAL INSTITUTIONS

In the first part of this chapter, a great deal of time was devoted to some material that educational institutions take for granted. Schools do not need help with lesson planning, presenting lessons, and evaluating training. These are their strong suits.

However, in workshops I present each year for educators, I find that they do need help in structuring courses to meet the needs of two groups: job preparatory students seeking the training necessary to enter CADD as an occupation and employed practitioners seeking training to update knowledge and skills in their fields. The needs of these two groups can be served well by educational institutions, but not with the same courses. The training needs of these two groups are too drastically different to allow one course to meet the needs of both.

This section presents those questions asked most often by educators seeking to become involved in CADD training as well as answers to these questions. Each answer will speak to both job preparatory training and updating training whenever appropriate

1. Should I teach drafting fundamentals first or in conjunction with CADD?
I strongly recommend teaching the fundamentals of design and drafting before teaching CADD. The argument is the same one that implores parents to let their children learn how to perform arithmetic operations manually before using a calculator. A drafter or designer still needs to know the fundamentals of design and drafting. Remember, CADD is just the latest aid to drafting and design. Students who have already learned such concepts as scaling, dimensioning, orthographic projection, axonometric projection, and descriptive geometry will learn CADD faster than those who haven't learned these concepts. I have had the best results waiting to introduce CADD until students have learned the fundamentals of design and drafting.

2. Should CADD be taught separately or within regular design and drafting classes?

The best answer to this question is some of both. I have had the best results using the following three-step approach in teaching CADD to job preparatory students: (1) Teach students drafting and design fundamentals; (2) Give students a course in CADD; and (3) Integrate CADD into the rest of the courses that make up the curriculum. The answer is, of course, different for updating practitioners. This group should be given a separate course that gets right to the heart of the matter and focuses on the special needs of this group. Self-paced learning scheduled conveniently around or after working hours is best for this group.

3. What traditional concepts can be dropped from the curriculum to make room for CADD?

Unfortunately, we are still in a transitional period. Students completing a drafting and design training program may still need manual skills for some time to come, particularly those who choose to work in small companies. This makes it difficult for teachers trying to fit CADD into an existing curriculum. What I have had to do is to shorten the amount of time I spend on certain concepts to make room for the time that must be spent on CADD. If students are taking a course in architectural drafting in which they have traditionally completed five projects manually, I have them do two manually and three on a CADD system. A point in time will eventually be reached when skills such as lettering and linework can be completely dropped from the curriculum. However, that time is not yet here.

4. How many workstations are needed per student?

This really depends on how the training is structured. Few schools have one system or workstation per student. This isn't even necessary. At one time, I was training 100 students per semester with only two systems. I did this by making the systems available by appointment only, from early morning until late at night five days a week. Now this was a little extreme, but it makes the point that even one system is enough to get started. However, if the open-lab concept by appointment only is used, one system for every five students is a comfortable ratio.

5. What topics should be covered in a course(s) on CADD for job preparatory students?

Job preparatory students are learning to be CADD users. Therefore they will need to cover material that is user oriented. This includes both knowledge-oriented and skills-development material. The following list is a comprehensive guide to the topics that, at a minimum, should be covered. The list is divided into two groups of topics: knowledge related and skills related.

Knowledge-Related Topics
Definition of the term "computer"
Various classifications of computers
Various sizes of computers
Differences between humans and computers
Various components of a typical computer system and what each component does
Benefits of the computer
Applications of the computer
Historical development of drafting and design from T-squares to computers
Definition of CADD
Impact of CADD on drafting and design
Future outlook of design and drafting with regard to the impact of CADD
Common myths about CADD and the corresponding realities
CADD-related concepts: CAD/CAM, CAE, CAED, CNC, and CIM
CADD systems
CADD hardware
CADD software
CADD users
CADD system processor technology
   Memory size
   Memory locations
   Memory types
   Memory mapping
   Parity memory
   Cache memory
   Virtual memory
   On-line storage
   Off-line storage
   Processor sizes (8, 16, 32, and 36 bit)
CADD input and interaction technology
   Keyboards
   Digitizers
   Function menus (tablet, screen, and keyboard types)
   Light pens
   Pucks

Joysticks
Thumbwheels
Trackballs
Voice activation
Direct screen interaction
CADD output technology
Text displays
Raster graphics displays
Directed-beam refresh graphics displays
Storage tube graphics displays
Pen plotters
Electrostatic plotters
Photoplotters
Hardcopy units (stand-alone and built-in)
Dot matrix printers
Impact printers
Evaluating CADD systems
Hardware configurations
Software capabilities of standard packages
Capabilities of add-on packages and costs of add-ons
Initial and continuing costs of systems
Best and worst applications of systems
Maintenance of hardware and software
Expandability of systems
Flexibility of systems (non-CADD applications)
CADD management
System selection
Hardware setup, startup, and testing
Software loading, startup, and debugging
Software backup
File management
User control and management

Skills-Related Topics
Keyboard skills
Cursor control
Tablet menu interaction
Screen menu interaction
Keyboard menu interaction
Entering commands, coordinates, etc., via the keyboard
Creating text

Manipulating text
Editing text
Creating graphic data
Manipulating graphic data
Modifying graphic data
Digitizing
Operating output devices
  Plotters
  Printers
  Hardcopy units

6. **What topics should be covered in a course for employed practition-ers?**
The same list presented above can be used as a curriculum development master. However, I strongly recommend when dealing with employed practitioners that the time and emphasis be placed on CADD management and hands-on skills development. Much of the knowledge base can even be left off for those who want a very short, concentrated course. I also recommend that two other topics be added for this group: justifying the CADD investment, and implementing the CADD conversion and making it work.

Chapter 8
ADVANCED CADD CONCEPTS

There are several advanced CADD concepts with which you should be familiar before being pronounced CADD literate, stated in the following questions:

1. What is wireframe 3-D drafting?
2. What is surface modelling?
3. What is solids modelling?
4. What is finite element modelling and analysis?
5. What is computer-aided manufacturing (CAM)?
6. What is CAD/CAM?

WIREFRAME 3-D DRAFTING

Wireframe three-dimensional drafting is the most readily available and least-expensive type of 3-D software package on the market. Most systems are capable of wireframe 3-D.

Wireframe 3-D drafting in CADD involves creating the simplest form of geometric model. A wireframe 3-D model is an isometric, dimetric, or trimetric representation of an object, shown in Figure 8–1. So a wireframe 3-D model is not a true 3-D model but a single-line facsimile of one.

Although a wireframe model does allow the user to see an objective in a representation that is easier to understand than 2-D orthographic views, there are problems with 3-D wireframe models. The less-expensive software packages show all lines (solid and hidden) as solid lines. Of course, this causes problems with understanding and interpreting what you are looking at. The better wireframe packages allow users to remove the lines that would be hidden in a manual drawing, resulting in a model that is easier to understand, such as those shown in Figure 8–1.

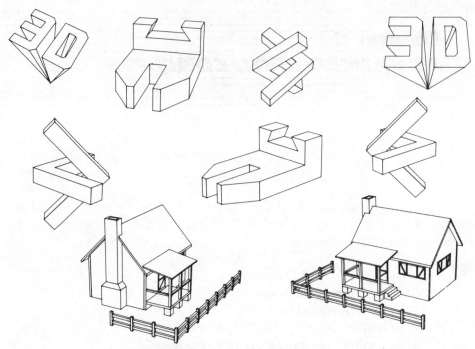

Figure 8–1   3-D wireframe models *(Courtesy T&W Systems Inc.)*

SURFACE MODELLING

Surface modelling is another method of creating geometric models. Its most common application is civil engineering and drafting for tasks such as creating models of topographical features. A surface model of a piece of land is much easier to comprehend than the traditional contour maps drafted manually. Surface modelling is a more complex type of modelling than 3-D wireframe.

CADD systems that have surface modelling software can convert traditional 2-D contour maps to 3-D surface maps. Figure 8–2 is an example of a surface model of a contour map. Examine the 2-D contour map in the background and then the 3-D surface models, and compare them for ease of understanding.

SOLIDS MODELLING

Solids modelling is the most expensive, most complex type of geometric modelling package available in CADD. Wireframe 3-D models represent only

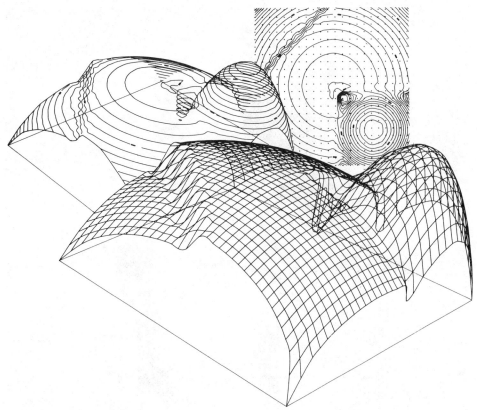

Figure 8–2   3-D surface model *(Courtesy AutoTrol)*

the edges of the subject. Surface models represent just the surface of the subject area. But solid models represent the entire object. A solid model constructed on a CADD system can take the place of a live model built manually.

Solid models can be used in any CADD application. However, they are used most frequently in manufacturing-related applications. Solids modelling offers designers several advantages. One is visualization. Some designers never become proficient in or comfortable with 2-D orthographic views of the subject of their design. Even those who do, find it much easier to visualize their design when represented more closely to the way the human eye actually sees things.

Figure 8–3 is an example of a solid model of a machine part. Figure 8–4 shows solid models displayed on the graphics terminal of a contemporary CADD system.

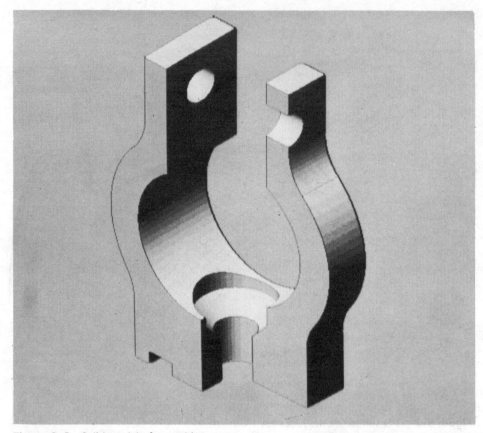

Figure 8–3 Solid model of a machine part

FINITE ELEMENT MODELLING AND ANALYSIS

You learned early in this book that geometric modelling can alter the five steps in the design process, specifically Step 4—Models or Prototypes. Finite element modelling and analysis is needed if computer models are to be substituted for live models or prototypes. Finite element modelling and analysis takes the concept of geometric modelling one step further and allows the structural elements of the part to be analyzed just as would be done with a live model or prototype.

The primary reason for building live models or prototypes is so they can be tested under actual conditions to determine if they perform according to specifications before they are mass-produced. Models and prototypes may be tested for their performance when subjected to stress, strain, temperature, pressure, the

Figure 8–4 Solid model displayed on the graphics terminal

elements, etc. These types of tests, of course, are destructive tests, making them an expensive undertaking.

Finite element modelling and analysis allows users to subject a part to the same forces and conditions through computer simulation rather than destructive testing. The results are recorded and analyzed. This is accomplished in three steps:

1. A 3-D solid model of the part in question is developed.
2. The solid model is converted into a finite element model by dividing it into numerous small subparts called finite elements.
3. The finite elements are subjected to the various forces and conditions through computer simulation, and the results of the performance of each finite element are recorded. The sum of the results for each element is the total performance of the part as a whole.

COMPUTER-AIDED MANUFACTURING (CAM)

Computer-aided manufacturing is a broad term used to encompass any manufacturing process that is automated or partially automated through the use of a computer. The most common concepts under this broad heading are:

- Computer numerical control (CNC)
- Robotics
- CAD/CAM

Computer Numerical Control (CNC)

The foundation of CAM is numerical control, or NC. To understand CNC, one must first understand NC. NC is a process in which machine tools are given instruction via a programmed medium that is run through a control unit. There are three components in an NC system:

1. The programmed medium
2. The control unit
3. The machine tool

The programmed medium might be any one of several different types of media, such as punched paper tape, punched cards, or magnetic tape. The medium chosen is programmed using a special code that is based on the *X-Y* or *X-Y-Z* coordinate system. One *X-Y* coordinate represents a position to the machine tool.

The programmed medium is fed through a control unit which reads the code, interprets its meaning, and issues instructions to the machine tool. These processes are all accomplished electronically.

As in manual manufacturing, the actual cutting, drilling, grinding, and turning processes are accomplished by machine tools. The difference is that in an NC system, the machine tools receive their instructions from the control unit rather than directly from a human machinist.

Computer numerical control (CNC) is an undated, modernized version of NC. There are still three components:

1. The programmed medium
2. The control unit
3. The machine tool

However, there are important differences between NC and CNC. In CNC, the control unit is replaced with a microcomputer or minicomputer. The computer still serves as the control unit, but it has one capability that NC control units do not have—storage.

Because of the computer's storage capability, the programmed medium is only fed through the control unit once. As it is fed through, it is stored and can be used for an unlimited number of the same part. In an NC system, the instructions must be fed through the controller for each part.

CNC machine tools look slightly different from their manual counterparts. One major difference, of course, is the presence of a microcomputer or minicomputer control unit. Figures 8–5 and 8–6 are examples of modern CNC machines.

Figure 8–5 is a horizontal spindle CNC machining center. Notice the control unit in front of the operator. It contains either a microcomputer or a minicomputer for storing programmed instructions.

Figure 8–6 is a vertical spindle CNC machining center. Once the instructions for a given part are stored, an unlimited number of the part in question can

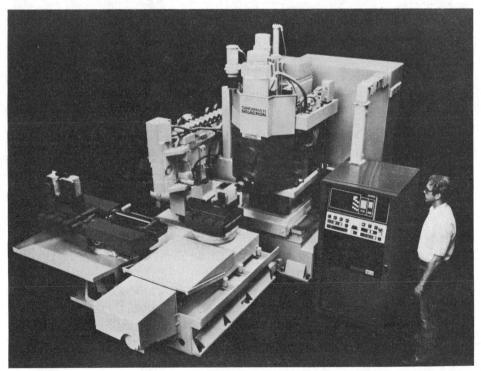

Figure 8–5   Horizontal spindle CNC machining center *(Courtesy Cincinnati Milacron)*

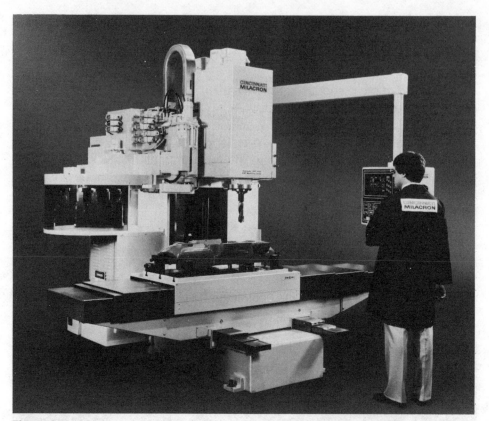

Figure 8–6 Vertical spindle CNC machining center *(Courtesy Cincinnati Milacron)*

be machined without re-entering the instructions. This, of course, saves both time and work. Figure 8–7 is a horizontal broach. Figure 8–8 is a CNC step grinder. The control unit is in evidence on the front of the machine. Finally, Figure 8–9 is a CNC grinding machine. Its control unit is also easily seen.

The broach, step grinder, and grinding machine are all traditional machine tools, the origins of which date back to before the Industrial Age. Although the machines themselves have improved continually over the years, their basic functions have remained unchanged. This is still true, even in the age of computer-aided manufacturing and high technology.

What *is* different about the machines shown in Figures 9–8, 9–9, and 9–10 is how they are operated. The manual predecessors of these machines are loaded, operated, and unloaded by human hands. In the ultramodern machine shop of today, they can be operated by computers and loaded/unloaded by robots.

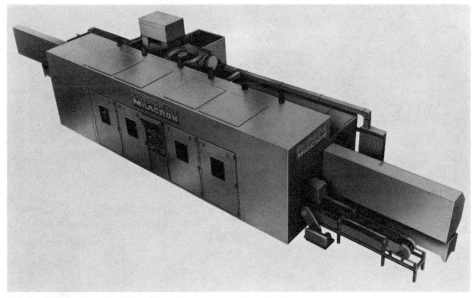

Figure 8–7 Horizontal broach *(Courtesy Cincinnati Milacron)*

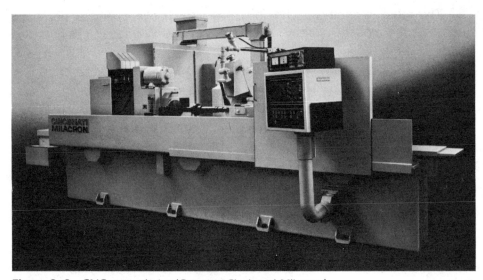

Figure 8–8 CNC step grinder *(Courtesy Cincinnati Milacron)*

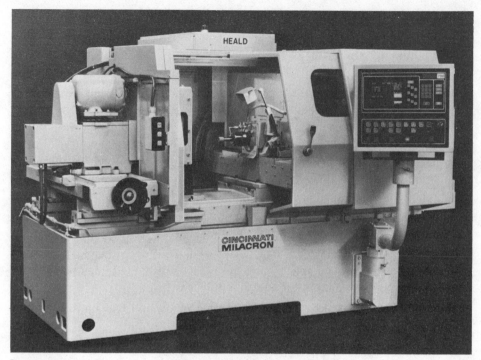

Figure 8–9 CNC grinding machine *(Courtesy Cincinnati Milacron)*

The robot is another technological device that is having a significant impact on the modern world of machining, as you will see in the next section.

ROBOTICS

Robots have been popular since the days of Buck Rogers. Because they have certain human-like characteristics—although these have been grossly exaggerated by Hollywood and television—robots have a natural appeal. Robots are nothing more than programmable electromechanical machines that can perform a specified number of tasks.

Industrial robots have been designed to be particularly suited for performing tasks such as loading machines, spot-welding, and even assembling certain products. Industrial robots operate according to stored programs that can be entered on-line as needed and altered to allow the robot to perform a new task.

There are several different types of industrial robots. They are categorized according to their motion systems and the types of manipulations of which they are capable. The four most common types of industrial robots are:

1. Cartesian coordinate robots
2. Polar coordinate robots
3. Cylindrical robots
4. Jointed-arm robots

As the name implies, a Cartesian coordinate robot has a range of movement parallel to the X, Y, and Z axes. This results in a range of movement that is confined within an invisible rectangular box.

A polar coordinate robot has a working area that is defined by a partial sphere. For this reason, polar robots are sometimes referred to as "spherical coordinate robots." Such a robot has a telescoping arm that moves up and down when manipulated by a pivot. A polar coordinate robot also has a rotary base.

A cylindrical robot has a stationary base on which is mounted a cylindrical body in a vertical format. The arm motion is in and out from the body as well as up and down in relation to it. The cylindrical body rotates on the stationary base.

A jointed-arm robot emulates the movements of the human arm. Just as a human arm has wrist, elbow, and shoulder joints, a jointed-arm robot has three corresponding joints, each with its own individual motions. In addition, the entire arm rotates on a stationary base.

CAD/CAM

One of the most frequently heard terms these days is CAD/CAM. This is the acronym for computer-aided design/computer-aided manufacturing. CAD/CAM involves joining the design and manufacturing processes after automating both. And it represents the optimum in productivity improvement if handled properly.

The functional bridge between CAD and CAM is the data base created when designing a part on a CADD system. When this same data base is used to develop the programmed instructions for CAM machine tools, the gap between CAD and CAM has been bridged.

A company can have an automated design and drafting department with CADD and an automated manufacturing department with CNC and robotics.

But until the two are joined, that company does not have CAD/CAM. And the productivity benefits of CAD/CAM can be significantly greater than the sum of the benefits realized from CAD and CAM separately.

With an understanding of such topics as wireframe 3D drafting, surface modelling, solids modelling, finite element modelling and analysis, and CAD/CAM as well as the material presented in the preceding chapters, readers can now be pronounced CADD literate. As a CADD-literate person, you will naturally be interested in what the future holds for CADD. This is the subject of Chapter 9.

Chapter 9
THE FUTURE OF CADD

The future of CADD will be characterized by continued growth, continued improvement, less-expensive prices for systems, and continued positive change. By the year 2000, CADD will be the norm rather than the latest development in design and drafting.

The trend in software will be toward more and more software development firms entering the market. This will result in more, better, and less-expensive software. Some of the more significant hardware developments to expect are:

Better graphics terminals. "Better" means higher resolution, faster response times, and higher-quality color.

Radical changes in packaging of graphics terminals as flat, thin picture tubes are developed.

Improvements in electrostatic copying technology will increase the popularity of this extremely fast method of plotting over pen plotting for producing hardcopy.

In addition to hardware and software developments, improvements can be expected in interaction technology. Two developments that can be expected in this area are:

- Coming of age of voice interaction in which users interact with CADD systems by talking. This technology is already available on a limited basis. Between now and the year 2000, it can be expected to become a feasible interaction method rather than a novelty.
- Direct screen interaction for selecting menu options or even controlling the cursor. This will allow users the option of interacting with the graphics display with a finger if they so desire.

All of these developments are important, but if the future of CADD had to be summed up in one word, that word would be **microCADD**. Computer-aided design and drafting on microcomputer-based systems can be expected to be the major development in CADD for the next 10 years.

The growth rate of microCADD is astonishing. As of January 1985, this market was expanding by over 60% per year. There are a number of reasons for the growth of microCADD:

Low Cost. MicroCADD is affordable even to small companies. Cost has been the major impediment to the growth of CADD in this country. Most firms that are large enough to afford mini or mainframe computer-based systems have moved into CADD or are in the process of doing so. However, the largest market is small firms that are involved in architecture, engineering, or manufacturing. These firms often cannot afford the larger CADD systems that dominate the market. However, they can afford microcomputer-based systems that can be purchased and made operational for under $20,000.

Simplicity. Whereas it might take 6 months to become proficient in operating the larger systems on the market, a practitioner can become proficient in the use of a microCADD system in 1–2 weeks. This cuts down on training time and the amount of productive time lost in a conversion due to learning curve problems. It also tends to enhance employee acceptance of CADD.

Familiarity. As a rule, people are becoming familiar with microcomputers. Consequently, they are no longer frightened by them. Many can even operate a microcomputer if for no other application than home computer games. This familiarity also tends to enhance acceptance of microcomputer-based CADD systems.

Training. Microcomputer-based CADD systems are excellent for providing low-cost CADD training. Many educational institutions are relying on micro-CADD to allow them to keep design and drafting programs up to date in spite of perennial budget problems.

Main System Relief. Most larger companies that turn out a high volume of documentation have two types of print machines: a large production machine and a smaller checkprint machine. The large production machine is only cost effective in turning out large volumes of work and cannot be efficiently turned on and off as needed for short runs. Short runs are handled on the checkprint machine, which can be turned on and off at will. This same problem exists with CADD. There are some small and less-complex jobs from which the larger mainframe CADD systems can be relieved. Microcomputer-based CADD systems can solve this problem for companies.

At present, numerous companies are involved in developing and marketing microcomputer-based systems. Typically these companies develop and market only software. They package or recommend hardware manufactured by other hardware companies. The type of hardware typically recommended by microCADD software companies is listed below with corresponding prices.

Hardware Device	Approximate Cost (1985 $)
Microcomputer with over 500K RAM and a hard disk	$ 5,000
Graphics terminal	1,000
Graphics tablet with puck	1,200
Plotter (D-size pen)	3,500
Miscellaneous (special card, cables, connectors, surge protection, etc.)	1,200
Training and installation	2,000
	$13,900

Such a configuration will allow a company to invest in a hardware configuration for under $14,000 (1985 dollars). This figure decreases as time goes by. This leaves only the microCADD software to purchase and, of course, prices vary.

At present, six companies are the leaders in the microCADD software development business. These vendors, their software packages, and approximate prices are listed below:

Vendor	Software Package	*Approximate Cost (1985 $)
T & W Systems Suite 106 7372 Prince Drive Huntington Beach, CA 92647 (714) 847-9960	VersaCAD	$2,500.00

Autodesk, Inc. 150 Shoreline Highway Mill Valley, CA 94941 (415) 331-0356	AutoCAD	$1,500,000
Personal CAD Systems Building B 918 University Avenue Los Gatos, CA 94030 (800) 882-7535	CADPlan	$2,000.00
BG Graphics 824 Stetson Avenue Kent, Washington 98031 (206) 852-2736	Drawing Processor II	$1,000.00
Computer-Aided Design 7650 Geary Blvd San Francisco, CA 94121 (415) 387-0263	MicroCAD	$1,000.00
Robo Systems Chessell-Robocom Corporation 111 Pheasant Run Newtown, PA 18940 (215) 968-4422	RoboCAD 2	$1,500.00

*Some prices include options beyond the standard package.

The list of companies involved in microCADD development will expand considerably during the next ten years. Correspondingly, the availability of high-quality software and hardware will go up while prices go down. This, in turn, will lead to more and more user companies becoming involved in CADD.

An examination of the prices listed above will show that, even now, a company can convert to CADD with an investment of less than $20,000 including hardware, software, and training. This is the most significant trend in the future of CADD.

GLOSSARY

A

access method   Any of the data-handling techniques available to the user for transferring data between main storage and input/out devices.

access time   The time interval between the instant at which data are called for from a storage device and the instant that delivery is completed.

accuracy   The degree of freedom from error. Averages and deviations are found by making many identical programmed moves and then checking them.

alphanumeric   Referring to the totality of characters that are either alphabetic or numeric.

alphanumeric character set   A set that contains letters, digits, and other characters.

analog   Pertaining to representation by means of continuously variable physical quantities.

analog computer   A computer in which analog representation of data is used.

application   A definable set of drafting tasks to be accomplished in a given drafting area. May be accomplished partly through manual procedures and partly through computerized procedures.

application software   Software designed to operate as a system for specific applications (i.e., architectural drafting).

assemble   To prepare a machine language program from a symbolic language program by substituting absolute operation codes for symbolic operation codes and absolute or relocatable addresses for symbolic addresses.

assembler   A program that assembles a symbolic language by translating symbolic operation codes into machine language and assigning memory locations for variables and constants.

attention key   A function key on terminals which causes an interruption of program execution by the central processing unit.

auxiliary storage   Storage that supplements main memory, such as disk, tape, drum, or virtual storage.

B

backspace   To move back the reading or display position according to a prescribed format. Can be used for erasing.

BASIC (Basic Beginner's All-Purpose Symbolic Instructional Code)   A simple computer language used for problem-solving by engineers, scientists, and others who may not be professional programmers.

benchmark   A point of reference from which measurements can be made.

binary code   A code that makes use of exactly two distinct characters, 0 and 1.

bit   The smallest unit of information, usually expressed as 1 or 0.

bit rate   The speed at which bits are transmitted, usually expressed in bits per second.

BPI   Bits per inch.

BPS   Bits per second.

brightness   The apparent level of intensity of illumination on a display service.

bug   A mistake or malfunction. An error or flaw in a program that renders it incapable of performing the objectives for which it was written. Debugging is the process of finding and eliminating programming errors.

byte   Group of eight bits. A sequence of adjacent binary digits operated upon as a unit. A series of computer binary "bits" organized together to hold a symbol, letter, or number in a computer. Sometimes called a "word."

C

CAD (Computer-Aided Drafting)   The use of computers and peripheral devices to aid in the documentation for design projects.

callup   A request by the user asking the computer to perform a certain function.

CAM (Computer-Aided Manufacturing)   The use of computers to aid in any and all phases of manufacturing. Numerical control (NC) is one form of CAM.

character   A letter, digit, or other symbol that is used as part of the organization, control, or representation of data.

character font   The style of the shape of a character; a lettering style.

character set   An ordered set of unique representation such as the 26 letters of the alphabet.

computer graphics That branch of science and technology concerned with methods of techniques for converting any form of information to or from graphic representation via computer.

computer programming language A set of precisely defined rules devised to greatly simplify communication with a computer (e.g., BASIC, COBOL, FORTRAN, PASCAL). The greater the power of a higher-level language, the greater the complexity of information that can by precisely conveyed in an efficient manner.

configuration The group of equipment and devices that makes up a CADD system.

coordinate An ordered set of data values, either absolute or relative, which specifies a location.

CPU (Central Processing Unit) A unit of a computer that includes circuits controlling the interpretation and execution of instructions.

cursor (1) On a CRT, a movable marker that is visible on the viewing surface and is used to indicate a position at which an action is to take place or the position on which the next device operation would normally be directed. (2) On digitizers, a movable reference, usually optical crosshairs used by an operator to indicate manually the position of a reference point or line where an action is to take place.

D

data A representation of facts, concepts, or instructions in formalized manner suitable for communication, interpretation, or processing by human or automatic means.

data base A collection of data comprised of comprehensive files of information having predetermined structure and organization.

data file A collection of related data records organized in a specific manner.

debug To detect, locate, and remove mistakes from a routine or malfunctions from a system.

dedicated Fixed in function or purpose.

device A piece of mechanical, electrical, or electronic equipment with a specific purpose.

digit For example, in decimal notation a digit is one of the characters from 0 through 9.

digital Pertaining to data in the form of digits.

digital computer A computer in which discrete representation of data is used mainly by performing arithmetic and logic processes on these data.

digitize To use numeric characters to express or represent data.

digitizer   A device for converting positional information into digital signals. Typically, a drawing or other graphic is placed on the measuring surface of the digitizer and traced by the operator, using a cursor.

digitizing   The conversion of points or lines into digital data as X-Y-Z coordinates.

disk   A storage device consisting of a number of flat, circular plates, each coated on both surfaces with some magnetizable material.

display   A visual presentation of data on an output device.

downtime   The time interval during which a device is inoperable.

drum plotter   A plotter that draws an image on a data medium such as paper of film mounted on a rotating drum.

DVST (Direct-View Storage Tube)   A type of graphic display.

E

edit   To rearrange data. To modify, insert, or delete characters.

editing   Modifying graphical data presented on the system display.

electrostatic plotter   A device providing hardcopy graphical and alphanumeric data on paper by means of electrostatic writing techniques.

entry   Each statement in a programming system.

erase   To obliterate information from a storage medium; to clear; to overwrite.

F

file   A repository of organized information consisting of records, items, or arrays, and data elements.

firmware   Programs loaded in read-only memory. A fundamental part of the system's hardware design, as contrasted to software, which is not fundamental to the hardware operation.

fixed-word-length computer   A computer in which data are treated in units of a fixed number of characters or bits.

flatbed plotter   A plotter that draws an image on a data medium such as paper or film mounted on a table.

format   A specific arrangement of data.

FORTRAN (FORmula TRANslation)   A high-level computer language mainly used for specific purposes.

function keys   Data-entry devices programmed to initiate or terminate a particular function or process in the graphic system.

G

graphic display   A raster, DVST, or vector display that can present an image to the user which has computer display.

graphic tablet   A rectangular planar surface to which a coordinate point can be transmitted by identifying it with a cursor in some manner. Same as *digitizer.*

grid   A defined array of horizontal and vertical lines that divides an area into uniform spaces called frames.

H

hardcopy   A copy of output in a visually readable form (e.g., printed reports, listings, documents, summaries, drawings).

hardware   The tangible equipment of the computer system.

I

IC (Intergrated Circuit)   An electronic device containing both active and passive elements in a single package.

initialize   To set a condition, routine, or word to its original state or state position.

input   The transfer of information into a computer or machine control unit.

input device   The device or collective set of devices used for conveying data into another device.

input/output (I/O)   A general term for the equipment used to communicate with a computer.

intelligent terminal   A terminal which has local processing power.

interactive   Processing of data on a two-way basis and with human intervention providing redirection of processing in a predetermined manner.

interface   The medium by which two separate elements are joined. An interface might be a hardware component to link two devices, or it might be a portion of storage or registers accessed by two or more programs.

internal storage   Addressable storage directly controlled by the CPU of a digital computer. See also *Main Storage.*

I/O device   Device used to transmit data to or receive data from the computer or secondary storage device.

L

light pen   A hand-held data-entry device used only with refresh displays. It consists of an optical lens and photocell, with associative circuitry mounted in a wand. Most light pens have a switch, allowing the pen to be sensitive to light from the screen.

M

main storage The general-purpose storage of a computer. Usually, main storage can be accessed directly by the operating registers.

matrix A logic network in the form of an array of input leads and output leads with logic elements connected at some of their intersections.

menu A list of options which is displayed on the CRT or on a plastic or paper overlay.

microcomputer A computer that is constructed using a microprocessor as a basic element of the CPU. All electronic components are arranged on one printed circuit board.

N

nonvolatile storage A storage that retains information when power is lost or turned off.

O

off-line operation Any operation carried on independently of the main computer.

on-demand system A system from which information or service is available at the time of request.

on-line operation Any operation carried on within the main computer system.

origin A reference point whose coordinates are relative zero.

output Data that have been processed from an internal storage to an external storage. Opposite of "input."

P

PASCAL (Phillips Automatic Sequence CALculator) A high-level computer language.

peripheral equipment Any piece of hardware, distinct from the central processing unit, used for input or output.

printer A device that prints the output of a computer.

processor The computer in a CADD system.

program A collection of one or more computer-executable procedures or instructions.

R

RAM (Random Access Memory) A monolithic or hybrid IC containing a functionally complete portion of a read-write memory, any of whose storage cells can be addressed.

refresh   To redraw the lines or images on the screen.

refresh display   A device that requires the refreshing of its screen presentation at a high rate in order that the image will not fade or flicker.

repeatability   A measure of the hardware accuracy of the retrace of a display element.

ROM (Read-Only Memory)   A storage device generally used for control programs whose content is not alterable by normal operating procedures.

rotate   To revolve through an angle relative to an origin.

rubber-banding   Technique for displaying a straight line that has one end fixed and the other end following an input device such as a light pen.

S

simulation   A technique in which a real process is represented by a simplified model.

software   A set of programs, procedures, rules, and possibly associated documentation concerned with the operation of a CADD system.

storage capacity   The amount of data that can be contained in a storage device.

storage device   A device into which data can be entered and held, and from which they can be retrieved at a later time.

symbol   A representation of something by reason of relationship, association, or convention.

T

terminal   A device in a CADD system through which data can either enter or leave.

turnkey system   A term applied to a computer system in which the supplier has total responsibility for building, installing, and testing the system, including hardware and software. A stand-alone system.

V

vector   A directed line segment which in computer graphics is always defined by its two end points.

viewing area   The area of the CRT face which can be directly seen by the console user.

W

window   A rectangular or square subset of the total display.

work station   The assigned location where a worker performs his or her job (i.e, the keyboard and system display).

APPENDIX

EDUCATIONAL INSTITUTIONS OFFERING CADD TRAINING

CALIFORNIA

Bulter Training Center
150 W. Iowa St.
Ste. #202
Sunnyvale, CA 94086
(408) 737-7525

California College of Arts and Crafts
Media Center
5212 Broadway
Oakland, CA 94618
(415) 653-8118

California College of Technology
Criss College
3301 W. Lincoln
Anaheim, CA 92801
(714) 952-8324

Golden Gate College
Computer Services Center
15744 Golden West St.
Huntington Beach, CA 92683
(714) 892-7711

Solano Community College
Suisun Valley RD
P.O. Box 246
Suisun City, CA 94585
(707) 864-7000

FLORIDA

Gulf Coast Community College
U.S. Highway 98 West
Panama City, FL 32401
(904) 769-1551

Okaloosa-Walton Jr. College
Technical/Industrial Education Dept.
100 College Boulevard
Niceville, FL 32578
(904) 678-5111

MICHIGAN

Eastern Michigan University
College of Technology
Dept. of Industrial Technology
Ypsilanti, MI 48197
(313) 487-2040

NEW YORK

Niagara County Community
College
4300 Buffalo Avenue
Niagara Falls, NY 14303
(718) 285-5235

Polytechnic Institute of New York
Computer Science Dept.
333 Jay Street
Brooklyn, NY 11201
(212) 643-5000

Pratt Institute
Office of Continuing Education
160 Lexington Ave.
New York, NY 10016
(212) 685-3745

Rochester Institute of Technology
College of Continuing Education
School of Applied Industrial Studies
City Center
33 N. Fitzhugh St.
Rochester, NY 14614
(716) 262-2736

OKLAHOMA

Oklahoma State Tech. College
Dept. of Drafting Technology
Fourth and Mission
Okmulgee, OK 74447
(918) 756-6211

PENNSYLVANIA

Pittsburgh Technical Institute
Computer Technologies Dept.
635 Smithfield St.
Pittsburgh, PA 15222
(412) 471-1011

WISCONSIN

Milwaukee Area Technical College
1015 N. Sixth St.
Milwaukee, WI 53203

CANADA

Durham College
Simcoe St. N.
P.O. Box 385
Oshawa, Ontario L1H7L7
(416) 576-0210

CADD DIRECTORIES

The following directories are available from the companies listed. They are valuable sources of in-depth information on specific CADD systems.

TURNKEY COMPUTER GRAPHICS
Daratech Inc.
P.O. Box 410
Cambridge, Massachusetts 02138

> Volume 1: Technical knowledge
> Volume 2: How to evaluate vendors and systems
> Volume 3: CADD vendors and their systems

THE S. KLEIN DIRECTORY OF COMPUTER GRAPHICS SUPPLIERS
Technology & Business Communications Inc.
P.O. Box 392
Sudbury, Massachusetts 01766

LOW COST CAD SYSTEMS AND A SURVEY OF CAD/CAM SYSTEMS
Leading Edge Publishing
11551 Forest Central Drive
Dallas, Texas 75205

CADD-RELATED ORGANIZATIONS

AMERICAN INSTITUTE FOR DESIGN AND DRAFTING
966 Hungerford Drive, Suite 10-B
Rockville, Maryland 20850
(301) 294-8712

AMERICAN SOCIETY OF MECHANICAL ENGINEERS
345 East 47th Street
New York, New York 10017
(212) 644-7100

NATIONAL COMPUTER GRAPHICS ASSOCIATION
2722 Merrilee Drive, Suite 200
Fairfax, Virginia 22031
(703) 698-9600

SOCIETY OF MANUFACTURING ENGINEERS
P.O. Box 930
Dearborn, Michigan 48128
(313) 271-1500

CONTEMPORARY CADD VENDORS AND THEIR SYSTEMS

Part of being well informed about CADD is knowing who makes what systems, in what price ranges, and for what applications. This type of knowledge becomes particularly valuable when it is time to purchase a CADD system. It's a lot like what you need to know when you want to buy a new car.

Most people planning to go car shopping can name the well-established automobile manufacturers, their major product lines, and approximate costs. Consequently, when it's time to buy a new car, they know where to go and who to see. Having this knowledge helps people avoid buying a station wagon when they needed a pickup truck. You need to be similarly informed when buying a CADD system too. This chapter will answer the following questions:

1. Who are the leading manufacturers of turnkey CADD systems in this country?
2. What systems do these companies manufacture and market?
3. What are the price ranges of these systems?
4. What are the most common applications for these systems?

There are approximately 100 vendors of turnkey CADD systems in this country, producing a wide range of systems in a wide range of prices for a wide range of applications. The list is not static; rather, new companies are constantly being added, and old companies that have failed or sold out are constantly being removed. However, there is a core of 25 companies that can be considered the leaders among CADD vendors.

These 25 companies and their systems are profiled in this section. The profiles are brief and not designed to provide the thorough information you must have before purchasing a CADD system from a company. Rather, the profiles should help you begin to prepare a list of those companies that might meet your needs but will need to be investigated more closely.

A person who is well versed in CADD should be familiar with these companies and their products. There is always danger in selecting just 25 companies from a list that often contains close to 100, but a line must be drawn somewhere. The criteria for determining which companies to include in the following profiles were:

1. Length of time in the CADD business
2. Approximate annual sales
3. Approximate market share

All three criteria were considered. Meeting just one would not necessarily mean that a company would be included. For example, a company that had been in the business a long time but had lower annual sales and a smaller share of the market would not be included over one that was relatively new but had greater annual sales and a larger piece of the market.

Using these three criteria, the companies profiled are those that have the best "track records" in CADD. The profiles are in alphabetical order rather than in order of sales, market share, or longevity. The data contained in each profile are readily available public information taken from marketing documents, company brochures, and annual reports. Each profile contains the following information:

1. An overview of the company and its CADD products
2. A list of the company's systems and approximate prices
3. The company's headquarters address and telephone number

Applicon

Applicon is a division of Schlumberger Technology Corporation based in Burlington, Massachusetts. It has been in the CADD business since 1969, making Applicon one of the early pioneers of CADD. Applicon produces three different turnkey CADD systems for a variety of applications, including mechanical design and drafting, electronic design and drafting, architectural design and drafting, civil engineering and drafting, and computer-aided manufacturing (CAM).

Applicon systems use 32-bit processors manufactured by Digital Equipment Corporation (DEC). The workstations for Applicon CADD systems center around a high-resolution raster display. Cursor control is by tablet, and menu options include tablet and screen varieties. The systems will support several different models and sizes of plotters as well as printers. The various software packages available with Applicon systems support two- and three-dimensional drafting as well as solids modelling. Applicon systems and their corresponding price ranges are as follows:

Systems	Approximate Price*
Series 4000/VLSI	$163,000–$400,000
Series 4000/IMAGE	$163,000–$400,000
BRAVO	$108,000–$600,000

*Actual prices in these ranges depend on the individual needs and options of the buyer.

Applicon manufactures, markets, installs, and services its CADD systems for buyers.

Applicon
32 Second Avenue
Burlington, MA 08103
(617) 272-7070

Auto-Trol Technology

Auto-Trol Technology Corporation is a firm based in Denver, Colorado, which has been in the CADD business since 1962. Auto-Trol Technology produces three different turnkey CADD systems, all of which can be used for a variety of applications, including mechanical design and drafting, architectural design and drafting, civil engineering and drafting, electronic design and drafting, and computer-aided manufacturing (CAM).

Auto-Trol Technology systems use 32-bit processors manufactured by either Digital Equipment Corporation (DEC) or Apollo. The workstations for Auto-Trol Technology systems center around a high-resolution color raster terminal. Cursor control can be achieved by tablet, joystick, and thumbwheels. Menu options include tablet and screen varieties. The systems will support a variety of different models and sizes of plotters. The various software packages available with Auto-Trol Technology systems support two- and three-dimensional drafting as well as solids modelling.

Systems	Approximate Price*
AGW 1	$100,000
AGW II	$60,000
AGW III	$91,000

*Actual prices depend on the individual needs and options of the buyer.

Auto-Trol Technology Corporation manufactures, markets, installs, and services its CADD systems for buyers.

Auto-Trol Technology Corporation
12500 N. Washington Street
Denver, CO 80233
(303) 452-4919

Bausch & Lomb

Bausch & Lomb Inc. is the same Bausch & Lomb that most people know as the manufacturer of contact lenses and other vision care products. Bausch & Lomb entered the CADD business in 1982. Since that time, it has developed and markets three different turnkey CADD systems, all of which can be used in three main application areas: mechanical drafting, architectural drafting, and education/training.

Bausch & Lomb systems use Digital Equipment Corporation (DEC) processors. The workstations for the systems include a high-resolution color raster terminal or terminals in one option. Cursor control is accomplished by horizontal and vertical thumbwheels. Menu options include tablet and push-button varieties. Bausch & Lomb systems will support a variety of different sizes and models of plotters. The software available for Bausch & Lomb systems is geared primarily for mechanical and architectural drafting, as well as training in these application areas, but will also support mapping and technical documentation.

Systems	Approximate Price*
Producer	$53,000 and up
Producer with dual rasters	$64,000 and up
ProDraft	$29,000 and up

*Actual prices depend on the individual needs and options of the buyer.

Bausch & Lomb manufactures, markets, installs, and services its CADD systems for buyers.

> Bausch & Lomb Inc.
> Interactive Graphics Division
> P.O. Box 14547
> Austin, TX 78761
> (512) 837-8952

BruningCAD

BruningCAD is a Tulsa, Oklahoma, division of the well-known AM Bruning International Corporation. The parent company has been in the engineering products business since 1924. However, the CADD line was not added until the 1980s. Since that time, BruningCAD has developed and markets five different turnkey CADD systems for use in three main application areas: mechanical drafting, architectural drafting, and education/training.

BruningCAD systems use 16- and 32-bit processors manufactured by Hewlett-Packard. The workstations for the systems center around a high-resolution color terminal. Cursor control is accomplished with a mouse. Menus are of the screen variety. BruningCAD produces its own plotters that interface in a variety of sizes with their various systems. Software packages available are designed primarily for mechanical and architectural drafting and training in these application areas.

Systems	Approximate Price*
EasyDraf2—Architectural	$41,000 and up
EasyDraf2—Mechanical	$45,000 and up
EasyDraf2—Educational	$16,500 and up

Systems	Approximate Price*
EasyThree (add-on feature to an existing system)	$2,500
AttriBase (add-on feature to an existing system)	$4,00

*Actual prices depend on the individual needs and options of the buyer.

BruningCAD manufactures, markets, installs, and services its CADD systems for buyers.

BruningCAD
6111 E. Skelly Drive
Tulsa, OK 74135
(918) 663-5291

CADAM

CADAM is a Burbank, California, company owned by Lockheed Aircraft Corporation. CADAM has been in the CADD business since 1982. Since that time, CADAM has developed and markets three turnkey CADD systems primarily for mechanical design and drafting, architectural design and drafting, and electronics design and drafting. By far the largest percentage of CADAM's sales are in the areas of mechanical design and drafting.

CADAM systems use 32-bit IBM processors. The workstation for the system centers around a graphics display that comes in a variety of choices including monochrome or color and of the raster or vector refresh types. Cursor control is accomplished with a light pen and tablet. Menus are of the screen variety. CADAM systems will support a variety of sizes and models of plotters. The software available for CADAM systems is designed primarily for mechanical and architectural applications with some available for printed circuit board design, drafting, and manufacture.

Systems	Approximate Price*
CADAM	$60,000 and up
Design-Build-Manage (DBM)	$21,000
Interactive PRANCE	$135,000

*Actual prices depend on the individual needs and options of the buyer.

CADAM develops, markets, and services only software. The company is not a hardware manufacturer.

CADAM, Inc.
1935 N. Buena Vista
Burbank, CA 91504
(818) 841-9470

CalComp

CalComp Systems Division of California Computer Products Inc. is a wholly owned subsidiary of Sanders Associates Inc. There are two aspects to CalComp in the CADD business. CalComp is well known for manufacturing individual and independent hardware items such as plotters and digitizers. However, Cal-Comp Systems Division manufactures and markets turnkey CADD systems. Cal-Comp Systems Division has five systems on the market covering the following applications: mechanical design and drafting, electronic design and drafting, architectural design and drafting, civil engineering and drafting, and map drafting.

CalComp Systems Division systems use 16-bit processors. The workstation centers around a high-resolution graphics display with color and monochrome options. Cursor control is accomplished with a light pen and tablet. Menus may be screen or tablet types. CalComp Systems Division CADD systems use Cal-Comp plotters. The software available is designed for architectural, mechanical, electronic, and civil applications.

System	Approximate Price*
IGS-500	$152,000 and up
IGS-400	$78,000 and up
Architectural software add-on	$7,500
Report writer software add-on	$7,500
P&ID/ISOMETRICS software add-on	$10,000 and up

*Actual prices depend on the individual needs and options of the buyer.

CalComp System Division's five systems are actually two hardware configurations and three software add-ons. CalComp Systems Division does manufacture, market, install, and service its systems for buyers.

CalComp Systems Division
2411 W. LaPalma Avenue
Anaheim, CA 92801
(714) 821-2011

Calma

Calma Company is a Santa Clara, California, CADD company owned by General Electric Company. Calma is one of the early pioneers of CADD, having been in the business since 1964. Calma has five turnkey CADD systems on the market being used in a wide range of applications, including mechanical design and drafting, electronic design and drafting, architectural design and drafting, civil engineering and drafting, mapping, and computer-aided manufacturing (CAM).

Calma systems use a variety of 16- and 32-bit processors, including processors manufactured by Digital Equipment Corporation (DEC), Data General, IBM, and Apollo. The workstations for Calma systems center around a high-resolution graphics terminal that comes in color and monochrome options. Cursor control is accomplished using a tablet. Menus may be screen or tablet types. Calma CADD systems will support a variety of sizes and models of plotters. The software available for Calma systems is designed for mechanical, architectural, electronic, civil, and mapping applications.

Systems	Approximate Price*
DDM	$100,000
GDS II	$250,000
DIMENSION III	$100,000
TEGAS ENVIRONMENT	$85,000
T-BOARDS	$100,000

*Actual prices depend on the individual needs and options of the buyer.

Calma Company manufactures, markets, installs, and services its various CADD systems for buyers.

Calma Company
2401 Tasman Drive
Santa Clara, CA 95050
(408) 970-1500

ComputerVision

ComputerVision, based in Bedford, Massachusetts, is one of the early pioneers of CADD, having started in the business in 1969. ComputerVision continues to be one of the top CADD companies in the world in terms of sales volume and number of systems placed. It has four turnkey systems on the market that are being used in a wide variety of applications, including mechanical design and drafting, electronic design and drafting, architectural design and drafting, civil engineering and drafting, mapping, technical documentation, and computer-aided manufacturing (CAM).

ComputerVision uses several different 32-bit processors, including processors manufactured by IBM. The workstations for ComputerVision systems center around a high-resolution graphics terminal that comes in monochrome and color options. Cursor control is accomplished with a tablet and mouse or light pen. Menus may be screen or tablet options. ComputerVision systems will support a variety of sizes and models of plotters. The software available for ComputerVision systems is designed for mechanical, architectural, electronic, civil, mapping, and technical documentation applications.

System	Approximate Price*
DESIGNER	$400,000 and up
CDS 4000	$400,000 and up
CDS 3000	$75,000 and up
CDS 5000	$485,000 and up

*Actual prices depend on the individual needs and options of the buyer.

ComputerVision manufactures, markets, installs, and services its various CADD systems for buyers.

ComputerVision Corp.
15 Cosby Drive
Bedford, MA 01730
(617) 275-1800

Control Data

Control Data Corporation is a well-known company in the business of computer products and services. The Computer-Integrated Manufacturing Division of Control Data, out of Minneapolis, manufactures and markets two turnkey CADD systems and several add-ons and services that can be used in a variety of applications, including mechanical design and drafting, electronic design and drafting, and computer-aided manufacturing (CAM).

Control Data processors come in 16- and 32-bit options that are either manufactured by Data General Corporation or built by Control Data. A typical workstation for a Control Data system centers around a high-resolution raster graphics terminal that comes in color and monochrome options. Cursor control is accomplished by tablet and thumbwheels. Menus come in tablet and screen options. Control Data systems will support a variety of sizes and models of plotters. The software available for Control Data systems is designed for mechanical, electronic, and manufacturing applications.

System	Approximate Price*
ICEM 800	$300,000 and up
ICEM 120	$45,000 and up

*Actual prices depend on the individual needs and options of the buyer.

Control Data manufactures, markets, installs, and services its CADD systems for buyers.

Control Data Corp.
Computer-Integrated Manufacturing Division
8100 34th Avenue South
Minneapolis, MN 55420
(612) 853-8100

Daisy

Daisy Systems Corporation in Mountainview, California, is a relatively new CADD company, having entered the business in 1980. Daisy manufactures and markets seven turnkey CADD systems dedicated to electronics design and drafting.

Daisy systems use 16-bit processors manufactured by IBM or built by Daisy. A typical workstation for a Daisy system centers around a high-resolution raster graphics display that comes in monochrome and color options. Cursor control is accomplished with a puck and tablet. Menus come in tablet and screen options. Daisy systems will support a variety of sizes and models of plotters. The software available for Daisy systems is dedicated strictly to electronics applications such as integrated circuit design and drafting and printed circuit board design and drafting.

System	Approximate Price*
LOGICIAN	$85,000 and up
LOGICIAN D	$100,000 and up
PERSONAL LOGICIAN	$17,000 and up
PERSONAL LOGICIAN AT	$25,000 and up
MegaLOGICIAN	$124,000 and up
PMX	$25,000 and up

System	Approximate Price*
GATEMASTER	$100,000
CHIPMASTER	$120,000

Daisy manufactures, markets, installs, and services its CADD systems for buyers.

> Daisy Systems Corp.
> 700 Middlefield Road
> Mountainview, CA 94039
> (415) 960-0123

Gerber Scientific

The Gerber Scientific Instrument Company is a South Windsor, Connecticut, company which manufactures and markets turnkey CADD systems for electronics applications, as well as pen and photoplotters that may be interfaced with the systems of other companies. Gerber Scientific manufactures and markets five turnkey CADD systems dedicated primarily to electronics design and drafting but also used to a lesser extent in architectural and mapping applications.

Gerber Scientific systems use 16-bit processors manufactured by Hewlett-Packard. A typical workstation for a Gerber Scientific system centers around a color graphics terminal. Cursor control is accomplished with a tablet and joystick. Menus come in display and push-button options. Gerber Scientific systems will support several sizes of plotters, but use primarily size D and E plotters manufactured by Gerber Scientific. Although software is available to a limited extent for architectural and mapping applications, Gerber Scientific software is mostly electronics design and drafting dedicated for printed circuit board design, drafting, and manufacture.

System	Approximate Price*
PC 800 Model 2	$50,000 or less
PC 800 Model 3	$50,000 and up
Model 78 System	$170,000 and up
Model 4135 Photoplotter System	$300,000 or less
AutoPrep 5000	$200,000 and up

*Actual prices depend on the individual needs and options of the buyer.

Gerber Scientific manufactures, markets, installs, and services its CADD systems for buyers.

Gerber Scientific Instrument Company
83 Gerber Road West
South Windsor, CT 06074
(203) 644-1551

Gerber Systems

Gerber Systems Technology, based in South Windsor, Connecticut, manufactures and markets CADD systems for mechanical design, drafting, and manufacturing applications. Gerber Systems Technology markets four turnkey systems.

Gerber Systems Technology uses 16-bit processors manufactured by Hewlett-Packard. A typical workstation for a Gerber systems CADD system centers around a raster graphics terminal that comes in color and monochrome options. Menus come in tablet and push-button options. Cursor control is accomplished with a tablet and joystick. Gerber Systems CADD systems will support a variety of sizes of plotters, all manufactured by Gerber. Software available for Gerber Systems CADD systems is designed primarily for mechanical applications.

System	Approximate Price*
AUTOGRAPH	$79,000 and up
SRM-1	$65,000 and up
IDS-80	$135,000 and up
IDS-3	$200,000 and up

*Actual prices depend on the individual needs and options of the buyer.

Gerber Systems manufactures, markets, installs, and services its CADD systems for buyers.

Gerber Systems Technology Inc.
40 Gerber Road East
South Windsor, CT 06074
(203) 644-2581

Graftek

Graftek is a relatively new company to CADD, having started in 1980. Based in Boulder, Colorado, Graftek is owned by Burroughs and manufactures and markets two CADD systems for mechanical design, drafting, and manufacturing applications.

Graftek systems use 32-bit processors manufactured by Digital Equipment Corporation, Hewlett-Packard, and Gould. A typical workstation for a Graftek system is centered around a color graphics terminal. Cursor control is accomplished with a tablet and joystick. Menus come in tablet, push-button, and display options. Software available for Graftek systems is dedicated to mechanical applications.

System	Approximate Price*
Series 32	$310,000 and up
Comet	$95,000 and up

* Actual prices depend on the individual needs and options of the buyer.

Graftek manufactures, markets, installs, and services its CADD systems for buyers.

Graftek Inc.
1777 Conestoga Street
Boulder, CO 80301
(303) 449-1138

Holquin

Holquin & Associates Inc. is an El Paso, Texas, company that has been in the CADD business since 1972. Holquin manufactures and markets five turnkey CADD systems for several different applications including mechanical design, drafting, and manufacturing; architectural design and drafting; civil engineering and drafting; and mapping.

Holquin systems use 16- and 32-bit processors manufactured by Hewlett-Packard. A typical workstation for a Holquin system is centered around a high-resolution raster graphics terminal that comes in color and monochrome options. Cursor control is accomplished with a tablet. Menus are available in tablet and display options. Holquin systems will support a wide variety of sizes and models of plotters. Software available for Holquin systems includes mechanical, architectural, civil, and mapping applications.

System	Approximate Price*
CEADS-CAD	$70,000 and up
DEADS-CIVIL	$20,000 and up
CEADS-GMS	$90,000 and up
CEADS-MACRO DESIGN	$90,000 and up
CEADS-UCCAPT	$30,000 and up

*Actual prices depend on the individual needs and options of the buyer.

Holquin Corp.
5822 Cromo Drive
El Paso, TX 79912
(915) 581-1171

IBM

It will come as no surprise to anyone that IBM is one of the leaders in manufacturing and marketing CADD systems since they are the world leader in the area of data processing. IBM manufactures and markets several CADD systems for applications such as mechanical design, drafting, and manufacturing; electronics design, drafting, and manufacturing; architectural drafting; and civil engineering and drafting.

IBM CADD systems use 32-bit processors manufactured by IBM. A typical workstation for an IBM CADD system centers around a high-resolution graphics terminal that comes in color and monochrome options. Cursor control is accomplished with a tablet and joystick. Menus are available in tablet, push-button, and display options. IBM systems will support a variety of sizes of plotters manufactured by IBM. Software available for IBM systems covers mechanical, electronic, architectural, and civil applications.

System	Approximate Price*
CADAM	$65,000 and up
CATIA	$65,000 and up
CAEDS	$65,000 and up
FASTDRAFT	$99,000 and up
CBDS2	$109,000 and up

*Actual prices depend on the needs and options of the buyer.

IBM manufactures, markets, installs, and services its CADD systems for buyers.

International Business Machines Corp.
Data Processing Division
1133 Westchester Avenue
White Plains, NY 10604
(914) 696-1900

IDI

Information Displays Inc. is an Armonk, New York, company that manufactures and markets a CADD system for mechanical drafting and technical publication applications as well as architectural drafting. It is best known for its technical publications applications.

IDI systems use 32-bit processors that they build themselves. The IDI system centers around a high-resolution color graphics terminal. Cursor control is accomplished using a tablet and light pen. Menus come in the screen variety only. The IDI system uses Hewlett-Packard plotters in sizes ranging from A to E. Software available for the IDI system is primarily designed for technical publications applications but can also be used for mechanical and architectural drafting.

System	Approximate Price*
IDRAW 3	$47,000 and up

*Actual price depends on the individual needs and options of the buyer.

IDI manufactures, markets, installs, and services its CADD system for buyers.

Information Displays Inc.
28 Kaysal Court
Armonk, NY 10504
(914) 273-5755

Intergraph

Intergraph, based in Huntsville, Alabama, has been in the business since 1969. Intergraph manufactures and markets three CADD systems for a variety of applications, including mechanical design, drafting, and manufacturing; electronics design, drafting, and manufacturing; architectural design and drafting; civil engineering and drafting; mapping; and technical documentation.

Intergraph systems use 16- and 32-bit processors. A typical workstation centers around dual high-resolution graphic terminals that come in color and monochrome options. Cursor control is accomplished using a puck and tablet. Menu options include tablet, push-button, and screen varieties. Intergraph systems will support a wide variety of sizes and models of plotters. Software available for Intergraph systems is designed for a wide variety of applications, including mechanical, electronic, architectural, civil, mapping, and technical documentation.

System	Approximate Prices*
INTERGRAPH 730	$78,000 and up
INTERGRAPH 751	$150,000 and up
INTERGRAPH 780	$270,000 and up

*Actual prices depend on the individual needs and options of the buyer.

Intergraph manufactures, markets, installs, and services its CADD systems for buyers.

Intergraph Corp.
One Madison Industrial Park
Huntsville, AL 35801
(205) 772-2000

MCAUTO

MCAUTO is a St. Louis, Missouri, CADD company owned by McDonnell Douglas Corporation, the well-known aviation company. MCAUTO is derived from the longer company name McDonnell Douglas Automation Company. MCAUTO manufactures and markets turnkey CADD systems and several software packages for mechanical design, drafting, and manufacturing; electronics design, drafting, and manufacturing; and architectural design and drafting.

MCAUTO CADD systems use 16- and 32-bit processors manufactured by Digital Equipment Corporation (DEC), Data General, and Prime. A typical workstation centers around a high-resolution color or monochrome graphics terminal that comes in raster, storage, and refresh options. Cursor control is accomplished through several means, including tablet and light pen, thumbwheels, and joystick. Menu options are either push-button, display, or both. MCAUTO systems will support a wide variety of plotter sizes and models. Software available for MCAUTO systems is designed for mechanical, electronic, and architectural applications.

System	Approximate Price*
UNIGRAPHICS II	$90,000 and up
ROBOTICS (1)	$95,000 and up
BDS/GDS	$100,000 and up

*Actual prices depend on the individual needs and options of the buyer.

MCAUTO manufactures, markets, installs, and services its CADD systems for buyers.

MCAUTO
McDonnell Douglas Automation Company
P.O. Box 516
St. Louis, MO 63166
(314) 232-2300

Mentor

Mentor is a Beaverton, Oregon, CADD company that has been in the business since 1981. Mentor manufactures and markets several systems that are used primarily for design as opposed to design and drafting. Mentor systems are used for design tasks such as analysis, review, and testing in the area of electronics.

Mentor systems use 16- and 32-bit processors manufactured by Apollo. A typical workstation centers around a high-resolution color or monochrome graphics terminal. Cursor control is accomplished with a puck and tablet and a special touchpad. Menus are of the screen variety. Mentor systems will support plotters in sizes from A to E manufactured by Hewlett-Packard or CalComp. Software for Mentor systems is designed for printed circuit board and integrated circuit design, analysis, review, and testing.

Systems	Approximate Price*
IDEA Station	$39,000 and up
Capture Station	$19,900 and up
Design Station	$29,900 and up
Test Station	$49,900 and up
DOC Station	$29,900 and up
MSPICE Station	$45,900 and up
GATE Station	$82,900 and up
CHIP Station	$89,900 and up
CELL Station	$82,900 and up

*Actual prices depend on the individual needs and options of the buyer.

Mentor manufactures, markets, installs, and services its CADD systems.

Mentor Graphics Corporation
8500 S.W. Creekside Place
Beaverton, OR 97005
(503) 626-7000

Prime

Prime Computer Inc., in Natick, Massachusetts, has been in business since 1972. Prime manufactures and markets turnkey CADD systems for mechanical and architectural applications.

Prime systems use 32-bit processors manufactured by Prime. A typical workstation centers around a high-resolution color graphics terminal. Cursor control is accomplished with a tablet, light pen, and joystick. Menus come in display and tablet varieties. Prime systems will support a wide variety of sizes and models of plotters. Software available for prime systems includes mechanical design, drafting, and manufacturing and architectural design and drafting.

System	Approximate Price*
PRIME PDGS	$75,000 and up
LOCAM	$135,000 and up
SAMME	$40,000 and up
GNC	$35,000 and up

*Actual prices depend on the individual needs and options of the buyer.

Prime manufactures, markets, installs, and services its CADD systems for buyers.

Prime Computer Inc.
Prime Park
Natick, MA 01760

Racal-Redac

Racal-Redac is a Westford, Massachusetts, CADD company that has been in the business since 1981. Racal-Redac manufactures and markets systems for electronics applications only.

Racal-Redac processors are 16- or 32-bit processors manufactured by Digital Equipment Corporation (DEC). A typical workstation is centered around a color raster graphics terminal. Cursor control is accomplished with a puck and tablet. Menus are the screen variety. Racal-Redac systems will support a wide variety of sizes and models of plotters. Software available covers printed circuit board design, drafting, and manufacture.

System	Approximate Price*
MAXI II	$99,500 and up
ADVANCED ROUTER	$50,000 and up
V800	$85,000

*Actual prices depend on the individual needs and options of the buyer.

Racal-Redac manufactures, markets, installs, and services its CADD systems for buyers.

Racal-Redac
4 Lyberty Way
Westford, MA 01886
(617) 692-4900

Scientific Calculations

Scientific Calculations Inc., based in Fishers, New York, is a CADD company that manufactures and markets systems dedicated to electronics applications. Scientific Calculations has been in the business since 1963.

Their systems use 32-bit processors that they build or that are manufactured by Digital Equipment Corporation (DEC) or Prime. A typical workstation for a Scientific Calculations system is centered around a raster color graphics terminal. Cursor control is accomplished with a puck. Menus are of the screen variety. Scientific Calculations systems will support a wide variety of sizes and models of plotters. Software available covers printed circuit board drafting and manufacturing and integrated circuit drafting.

System	Approximate Price*
SCICARDS	$50,000 and up
SCHEMACTIVE	$25,000 and up

*Actual prices depend on the individual needs and options of buyers.

Scientific Calculations manufactures, markets, installs, and services its CADD systems for buyers.

Scientific Calculations Inc.
7635 Main Street
Fishers, NY 14453
(716) 924-9303

Sigma Design

Sigma Design is an Englewood, Colorado, company that specializes in manufacturing and marketing CADD systems for architectural and civil applications. Sigma Design has been in the CADD business since 1975.

Sigma Design CADD systems use 16- and 32-bit processors manufactured by Sun Microsystems. A typical workstation for the Sigma Design system centers around a high-resolution graphics terminal that comes in color and monochrome options. Cursor control is accomplished with a tablet and joystick. Menus are of the push-button and tablet varieties. Sigma Design CADD systems use D size plotters manufactured by Hewlett-Packard or CalComp. Software available covers architectural design and drafting and civil engineering and drafting.

System	Approximate Price*
SIGMA III	$65,000 and up

*Actual price depends on the individual needs and options of the buyer.

Sigma Design manufactures, markets, installs, and services its CADD system for buyers.

Sigma Design Inc.
7306 S. Alton Way
Englewood, CO 80112
(303) 773-0666

Summagraphics

Summagraphics (Fairfield, Connecticut) has been in the CADD business since 1973. Summagraphics manufactures and markets CADD systems for the mechanical, electronics, architectural, and civil applications.

Its systems use 16- and 32-bit processors manufactured by Data General. A typical workstation centers around a high-resolution raster graphics terminal that comes in color and monochrome options. Cursor control is accomplished with a tablet. Menus are of the tablet variety. Summagraphics systems will support a wide variety of sizes and models of plotters. Software available for Summagraphics systems covers mechanical drafting; printed circuit board design, drafting, and manufacturing; architectural design and drafting; civil engineering and drafting; and education and training.

Systems	**Approximate Price***
ICON 2000	$49,500 and up
8000 Series	$70,000 and up

*Actual prices depend on the individual needs and options of the buyer.

Summagraphics manufactures, markets, installs, and services its systems for buyers.

> Summagraphics Corp.
> 777 State Extension Street
> Fairfield, CT 06430
> (203) 384-1344

Synercom

Synercom is a Sugar Land, Texas, company that manufactures and markets CADD systems dedicated to mapping applications. Synercom has been in the business since 1969.

Synercom systems use 32-bit processors manufactured by Digital Equipment Corporation (DEC). A typical workstation for a Synercom system centers around a raster graphics terminal that comes in color and monochrome options. Cursor control is accomplished with a puck and tablet. Menus are of the tablet, push-button, and screen varieties. Synercom systems use CalComp and Hewlett-Packed plotters ranging in sizes from A to E. Software available for Synercom systems is designed specifically for mapping.

Systems	**Approximate Price***
INFORMAP II	$40,000 and up
OPIS/3	$25,000 and up

*Actual prices depend on the individual needs and options of the buyer.

Synercom manufactures, markets, installs, and services its CADD systems for buyers.

> Synercom Technology Inc.
> 10405 Corporate Drive
> Sugar Land, TX 77478
> (713) 240-5000

Telesis

Telesis Systems Corporation in Chelmsford, Massachusetts, has been in the CADD business since 1980. Telesis manufactures and markets several turnkey CADD systems for mechanical and electronics applications.

Telesis systems use 16- and 32-bit processors that they manufacture themselves or that are manufactured by IBM or Digital Equipment Corporation (DEC). A typical workstation for a Telesis system centers around a color raster graphics terminal. Cursor control is accomplished with a light pen. Menus are of the screen variety. Telesis systems will support a variety of different sizes and models of plotters. Software for telesis systems covers mechanical design and drafting and printed circuit board design, drafting, and manufacture.

System	Approximate Price*
EDA 300 PCB	$78,600 and up
EDA 100 MECH	$49,500 and up
EDA 150 MECH	$36,000 and up

*Actual prices depend on the individual needs and options of the buyer.

Telesis manufactures, markets, installs, and services its CADD systems for buyers.

Telesis Systems Corp.
Two Omni Way
Chelmsford, MA 01824
(617) 256-2300

INDEX